Natural
Sheep Care

Natural Sheep Care

Pat Coleby

Acres U.S.A.
Austin, Texas

Natural Sheep Care

Acres U.S.A.
P.O. Box 91299
Austin, Texas 78709 U.S.A.
(512) 892-4400 •fax (512) 892-4448
info@acresusa.com • www.acresusa.com

Printed in the United States of America

Publisher's Cataloging-in-Publication

Coleby, Pat
Natural sheep care / Pat Coleby. Austin, TX, ACRES U.S.A., 2006
    xiv, 226 p. 23 cm.
    Includes bibliographical references and index.
    ISBN: 0-911311-90-4 (trade)

1. Sheep. 2. Sheep — Nutrition — Requirements. 3. Sheep — Health. 4. Sheep — Breeding. I. Title.

SF375.C65 2006   636.300994

This book is dedicated to the memory of the late 'Darkie' Day; a much respected 'gun' shearer and partner of my daughter, who is a wool classer. He was a man of great courage.

Acknowledgements

Thanks to all of the following:

The late Malcolm Adams for passing on much interesting information and arranging many photographs. Bryan Baker for his very helpful advice. Bob Crauford for information on footrot and keratin. Dr. Richard Evans, Veterinary Surgeon, for information on the 'Yellows'. Doug Harrison for enlightening me about sheep tag colors. Graham Holton, wool classer extraordinaire, for endless information and photographs. Keith Jones for allowing me to photograph his Romneys. Jo Hortin, my youngest daughter and a woolclasser, for help when I needed it. My sister-in-law, Venetia Jones, for Haddon Rig memories. The late Ian Loydd, for extracts from his article "A Constructive Look at Saltbush," in *Biological Farmers of Australia Newsletter*, March 1994, and for information supplied in discussions. Robert Partridge, Stawell for extended loan of G. Claude Notman's book. Wally Pederick for photographs and allowing me to take pictures of his prizewinning Corriedales. John Williams for making available the blood serum readouts from his animals, which meant we could formulate the original lick. The Wool Quality Project: Drs. Kevin Bell, BVSc. (Hons) PhD, Timothy J Watts, BVMS, MVS, Robert Woodgate BSc. BVMS for information on OS. And to any I may have missed, many thanks.

Contents

Foreword

In 1995 this book came out in Australia in a rather abbreviated version; then again much updated in 2000. Each time I do a new edition of my various books I think it is all there. But it never is. Thus in this 2006 version, updated and altered for American conditions and history, there is material that was not in any of the previous books — yet again. In particular, the sections on minerals and vitamins and other new (or old, whichever way one looks at it) remedies have been largely updated.

The actual text has been similarly altered where necessary as I never find out until after a book is published that the parts I think quite easy to understand apparently are not. This book also contains an extra chapter on land management and analysis which I did not think necessary for the first version in Australia. It is of course the most important of the lot.

My acquaintance with sheep all started when my family and I came to Australia as "ten quid trippers" (migrants from the U.K. — passage for adults was ten pounds sterling; children's passage was free) in 1959. We went straight to a grazing property, which ran Border Leicesters, Corriedales, beef cattle and thoroughbred stock horses. Prior to that I had only met sheep as a child, confined to watching the shepherds looking after my father's Sussex sheep, doing everything the English way, like lambing them in folds (movable artificial pens made from wooden hurdles on root crops, young cereals, kale or whatever was available) hand-shearing in those days and the ever-important agricultural show preparation once a year.

The first 20 years in Australia of looking after and helping with the landlord's sheep, spending many hours in the saddle watching for and treating blown sheep, did nothing to endear to me a species that, as far as I was concerned, let itself be eaten alive without a word of complaint. I also reared stud orphans of different breeds (using goat's milk) for local farmers. Some of these were delightful animals and one horned Dorset ram would come galumphing over to the road fence six years later, when I called as I rode past.

Then I really got to know the aristocrats of the business, working with merino farmers from Victoria to West Australia, and the more I learned, the more fascinating the mechanics became. I realized the poor suffering sheep of the early years should not have been afflicted at all, and the endless lambs I pulled in that district for other farmers should not have happened either.

This book is for all breeders of sheep, whatever their kind, small flocks or large, especially milk sheep. In Australia, this is a fast growing industry right now, meat or wool, we need them all — and wool is a natural fibre that has no equal.

So I hope that this book will help those in the United States as it seemed to help sheep farmers in Australia, who struggle on, despite the recessions and droughts, breeding and caring for a quite fascinating and generally rewarding animal. In the words of Graham Holton, sheep classer extraordinaire in Australia: "It's all in the feeding, Pat." It is indeed. No matter how good the breeding, without Graham's dictum — which does not just refer to minerals, shedded and housed sheep, but to the state of the fields and spreads where they run — a shepherd will produce an inferior flock.

I owe thanks to the Walters family of Acres U.S.A. for finally stirring me up to produce this edition for sheep farmers in their country, who in many respects are not so very different from those in Australia and other countries — quite surprisingly so.

— *Pat Coleby, Maldon, Victoria, Australia, 2006*

Chapter 1

Origins and Uses of Sheep

In the big grazing countries of the world (which include Russia) sheep for meat and wool have two connotations, according to which kind you farm. If it is Merinos you raise, all the others are referred to as crossbreeds. To those of you who farm these same crossbreeds, they are Border Leicesters, Suffolk, Southdown, Poll Dorset, Lincolns, Texels, Dorpers or one of many other breeds providing meat, skins and warmth to a large part of the population, especially in the early days.

But Merinos are just that — Merinos. They are the fine wool sheep; some would say the aristocrats of the species. With the tightening of the wool market in recent years, partly due to poor administration, superfine wool sheep have increased in popularity. The two breeds which have been evolved from Merinos are Corriedales and Polwarths and they come somewhere in between. They are known as strong-wool sheep and are usually very fine specimens indeed.

Now in the two "new world" countries we also have milk sheep, this is a farming enterprise which has been quite common in Europe for centuries, particularly for cheeses. It has only become popular and viable in Australia comparatively recently; maybe also in the States for the same reason because we are all becoming multicultural, and people like to have food similar to that of their country of origin. The most sought after products are usually yogurt, cheese, quarks and so forth. There are many people supplying what appears to be a sound and growing market. Sheep yogurt is more bland than that of goats or cows and does not seem to need additives to make it popular to modern palates, which is an advantage. Generally the bigger framed merino crosses are milked. However, it is a matter of choice and, as in all milking enterprises, sheep are already being bred with their milk potential in mind.

Crossbreeds often produce quite distinctive wool, some of which is used for particular purposes, such as the Drysdale, Tukidale and Lincoln, which are used for carpet-wools. Since writing the original sheep book in 1994, the demand for pure wool mattresses, pillows, cushions, etc. has increased greatly.

The merino fleece is unsuitable for this purpose as it too soft for the pillows or cushions to keep their shape. Therefore the strong wool and carpet sheep fleeces, which make excellent mattresses, have come into their own. All these are extremely comfortable and are finding a good market.

All sheep are to a point generally dual purpose, Leicesters, Corriedales and Polwarths bred up from Merinos are considered the most useful in this regard. Meat sheep fleeces are mostly used on the skin for clothing, rugs and footwear, but they still produce tough serviceable wool. Their usefulness lies in *all* their products.

There is now another important use for wool and that is for house in-wall insulation, either as batts or to be blown into the wall cavities. It is not flammable, does not collect vermin and appears to last well without collapsing like many other artificial materials. I have done one wall with it and the difference is most marked, it is certainly more efficient than any other insulation I have met. At present in Australia it carries a reasonably high price tag, which is offset by the advantages already mentioned and the fact that it seems to last indefinitely if properly installed.

In my youth I lived in the Isle of Man (United Kingdom). The Soay sheep on the Island produced a heavy, greasy wool which we knitted up into jerseys for seagoing fishing. They were like suits of armor and were totally impervious to wind and water. They smelt strongly of sheep's grease in spite of being washed numerous times — such a garment could never be made from a Merino's fleece — but they were, and possibly still are, indispensable for seagoing garments. So at the opposite ends of the scale, each breed of sheep has its use; the sheep is a truly remarkable animal in that it feeds and clothes quite a large part of the world's population and to date defies all imitators. Other uses for wool now include the above-mentioned batts for houses; mulch mats for commercial and ordinary gardeners, self-composting flower pots and the despised dags (that is, the dirty bits from the edge of the sheared fleece or from crutching to keep the wool around the rear-end clean) make excellent, long-lasting mulching material for trees.

Amazingly in Australia for many years the Wool Board had the weird idea that wool should only be sold to use on its own, a policy which must have lost a great many potential sales. Anyone who wears the extremely fine wool/silk and wool/cotton underclothes now made, and the often stretch wool/cotton denim type trousers as well as fine-wool suiting will know how incredibly comfortable they are. Similarly the wool/cotton denim jeans are doing very well. All these innovations have been and continue to be equally successful.

To a point the Alpaca and Angora industries have opened the eyes of sheep farmers to this kind of value-adding. Many farmers now are prepared to do some of this on farm, often rescuing old machinery to extremely good purpose. Value-adding of this type has been something that Anglo-Saxon farmers have been slow to pick up. To most European farmers it has been a way of life for a very long time.

There is another by-product of the sheep industry as well as wool, meat and skins, and that is lanolin. It is a very valuable base for many ointments and creams, but unfortunately like many fats it stores undesirable chemicals. It is now realized these are residual and persist after scouring and cleaning so that they can affect those who use the creams — medicinal or cosmetic. Now we have a strong case for chemical-free wool and the demand is increasing. This may sound like a contradiction in terms, because one would imagine wool to be one of the most natural materials available; not so, it can be and is polluted like practically everything else on earth.

To produce wool free of all pollutants and chemicals it has been necessary to raise the mineral content of the sheep diet (and ultimately hopefully the soil on which they feed) so those materials do not have to be used at all.

A host of disease conditions including (in Australia) fly strike, worms, lice and all interior protozoa-type illnesses as well as fungal (footrot and scald) and wool problems, Johne's Disease, and interior and exterior parasites, are all due to mineral imbalances or shortfalls in the diet. This is due to the level of degradation to which many of old sheep runs in Australia have sunk; and as will be seen later in this chapter they did not have very far to go. The land has reached such a low ebb that the necessary nutrients are unobtainable and the sheep cannot possibly be maintained in good health without using polluting chemicals. These are used either for worming or keeping them free of lice and other parasites.

In 1988 I worked in West Australia for three weeks putting in place a protocol so that chemical-free wool, which was being demanded by Europe so that *clean* lanolin for cosmetic and medicinal use could be available. Fortuitously, wool was at that time at an incredibly low ebb, so the farmers, if they were to survive as sheep grazers, had to change their ways. I met a fair amount of flak, but the idea caught on and they started using free-take minerals as well as bringing their land into line and forsaking artificial NPK fertilizers. These were by their very nature inhibiting nearly every mineral necessary for good health, particularly copper and cobalt.

Nowadays many sheep farmers, as well as putting out the necessary mineral licks, are engaged in land reclamation so that some of the valuable macro and trace minerals will hopefully become available again to be utilized by the animals.

Sheep also have another charactcristic — they are, if badly farmed, wreckers of land. One of the great grazers of southeast Victoria (Australia), G. Claude Notman wrote an excellent book (privately printed and now difficult to obtain) entitled *Of Sheep and Men*. It is an exhaustive history (the research must have been never ending) on the Merinos and the people who farmed them in the southern parts of Australia in the 1800s. He puts forward an interesting view on page one of the book. He suggests that the preoccupation of the rich Spanish landowners with the fortunes to be made from fine wool are the chief cause for the arid nature of most of Spain. Sheep eat down to the heart of the grass including the roots, and, if allowed to do so unchecked will finally eat the roots as well. They have to if they are to survive. This performance combined with the churning up of the ground by their small hooves will cause desertification and erosion in fairly short order, and does not happen if they are properly farmed. Think back to the early wars in the United States between the cattlemen and the sheep grazers — they each had a point.

When I first came to Australia we lived northeast of Melbourne. Our landlords, three wise and venerable brothers, farmed sheep, horses and cattle. Their farm ran alongside a large ranch that carried only sheep. Our landlords ran the larger head of stock and the land areas on the two properties were similar. Riding down the boundary fence was an education. On our side the grass was plentiful and varied and no erosion was visible because the landlords were good stockmen and changed the sheep from one area to another often. They also alternated their sheep with cattle between the two farms they owned, thereby keeping the feet of both herds in good order also by being on the roads every few weeks. On the other side of the fence apparently nothing was done except the absolute minimum necessary to keep the wool check coming. There was bare ground and gully erosion of dreadful proportions — up to 30 feet deep in places. The owner of that particular station spent his life traveling the world, leaving a manager who was expected to work miracles in his absence. You only get out of farming what you put into it and he put in nothing except the bare necessities to enable him to draw the wool check each year. Sheep farming does not have to be damaging to the environment, and hopefully nowadays that kind of farmer has virtually gone out of business.

In a later chapter I will describe why many badly farmed soils are so low in the lime minerals. In Australia this inherent deficiency is one of the chief causes of the low or unavailable trace elements and major minerals which generally go hand in hand with an excessively low or high pH. I work with an appreciable number of farmers in the United States and elsewhere, and the habitual good pH levels in other countries must be what makes the difference between the presence of the scourge of sheep or any wool-bearing animal in Australia — the dreaded fly strike. Hence my remark in the foreword about watching sheep being eaten alive (by maggots). Here, in the past and even today on farms that are sick enough, fly-strike is one of the greatest problems in this country of hot and often humid weather allied to poor soils. It is always far worse on paddocks which are deficient in the lime minerals and also have an unbalanced pH (the two do not always go together). Quite dramatic improvement in the fly strike incidence has been reported by farmers who have made the loose mix lick minerals mentioned in chapters five and eight available to their sheep, either with feed or in licks at all times.

The ultimate is, of course, to have the top-dressing done after having the soil analyzed. But on spreads where that would not be practicable, the presence of the licks has been very satisfactory. Because licks provide all the necessary minerals, they have also helped the country regenerate to a degree as the sheep will spend longer lying down each day, and sheep, like goats, will eat all the new growth of bush or scrub if they are deficient in copper. Even when land is fully remineralized the licks are still needed. Here soils are not strong enough to carry adequate minerals for European type stock. This is *not* the case in the United States, and I have talked this over with several people and all attribute the presence of our fly problem to inherently low calcium and magnesium in this country.

Chapter 2

History

Neither the Americas nor the antipodes had indigenous sheep; it is perhaps surprising that the Spaniards did not consider trying their valuable Moedinos in their new colony, but perhaps it never became settled enough for the experiment. There is a report that in 1783 the *Daedulus*, bringing sheep to the colonies obtained them in Vancouver from a Spanish settlement at Monterey. They picked up both sheep and hogs and landed them at Port Jackson, Sydney (J.C. Garran and L. White). It would be interesting to know how those sheep got there.

However a 1900 *Cyclopedia of Livestock and Complete Stock Doctor,* largely sourced from the United States in spite of being printed in Melbourne, Australia, mentions *Ovis montana,* or wild sheep of that district. Apparently several United States animals were shown in the Paris exhibition of 1865, and these were housed and tame. I owe nearly all the information on early breeds in the US to this same work.

The name Merino derives from an Arabian tribe, Moedinos, and presumably they first kept this type of sheep. The Arabs (Moors) have at various times occupied parts of Europe, and certainly they held large portions of Spain before and during the Middle Ages — and probably introduced their Moedino sheep at the same time. Referring back to H.B. Carter's *His Majesty's*

Merino ram, two years, bred by Graham Holton.

Spanish Flock, there is an illustration that shows the dispersal of Merinos from their original home in Spain, and their methods of entry into the United Kingdom during the latter part of the 18th and the early 19th centuries. They certainly traveled by circuitous routes.

Claude Notman in his history of the Merino breed, *Of Sheep and Men,* said that the first Merinos to leave Spain after the Napoleonic Wars went to Sweden. By far the greatest acquisitions of these Spanish sheep at that time were as profits or reparations of war. Also large numbers were obtained by the French Imperial Studs — from which descend the famous Rambouillet strain. This breed was known from the earliest times as producers of the finest wool. The Spanish government actually forbade the export of any of the sheep. It was not until 1786 when the King of Spain, in reply to a request from the French government, allowed the first sheep to actually leave the country. Three hundred and fifty-nine carefully selected rams and ewes were sent to Rambouillet farm near Paris, where, according to government records, they have been bred pure since 1801. They were also introduced to Germany during the last quarter of the 18th century. This is why many present-day American Rambouillets can trace their ancestry back to either the German von Homeyer flocks or those from Rambouillet, France.

According to the *Cyclopedia*, written in 1900 and cited above:

> The principal breeds of fine wooled sheep are: the
> Spanish, the Saxony, the Silesian, the French Merinos and
> the American Merinos. This last, now famous all over the
> United States is the result of careful breeding from
> Spanish stock, others of those breeds mentioned above
> had been tried but nothing equaled the Spanish lines.
> They say that the breed was by then so widely disseminat-
> ed in the State that they were divided into three 'families';
> those owned and bred by Silas Rich of Vermont; the
> Atwood and the Hammond Merinos which were originally
> pure Infantado or Paular blood from Spain.

These were characterized by the great looseness of the skin
which "lay in soft, low, rounded ridges over the body, but offering
no obstruction to the (hand) shears." In Australia, this became a
major problem because of the high incidence of fly strike, and the
wrinkles were eventually bred out. The enormous amount of damage from this source is partly due to the fact that the land in
Australia was, by comparison, extremely poor mineral-wise when
compared to that in the United States. Acidity and fly strike tend
to go hand-in-hand.

About 1809 William Jarvis, United States consul at Lisbon,
bought 50,000 sheep from the flocks of the Paulars (mentioned
above), and they with the Infantados make up the five families
which in 1900 constituted the base for the American Merinos —
"then acknowledged as some of the most valuable fine-wooled
sheep in the world." The descendants of the Infantados were a
large, compact and rather long-bodied lot. The descendants of the
Paulars are smaller but exceedingly rich in "all that constitutes fine
wool."

I have quoted some of this early history because even in
Australia today, where perhaps too much cross breeding of the
Merino lines has taken place, it is quite definitely possible to pick
out those two differing early types, especially among a mixed
flock. For a similar phenomenon, in thoroughbred racehorses
descended from three outstanding stallions with Barb and Arabian
blood in the late 1700s, occasionally the absolutely pure Arab type

occurs — out of the blue — even now. They were nearly always outstanding individuals.

An almost equal number of Merinos went to England from mercantile and trade transactions, most going to His (British) Majesty's Spanish Flock. There were also a significant number of what are referred to as "contraband or doubtful transactions." Not all the sheep rustling occurred in the colonies. Suffice it to say Merinos left the continent of Europe for all kinds of destinations including Iceland, Russia, South Africa, the United States and, of course, Australia (New South Wales) as well as the British Isles.

At the beginning of the 20th century up until World War I, Australia and Russia had the largest numbers of sheep in the world — 165 million head and 133.9 million head respectively. At that time sheep numbers were actually declining in the United States and South Africa. The last importations to Australia of Merinos came from the US between 1900 and 1905.

There is no record of stock improvement programs in those far-off days, but even then there were much prized families, rather like the three great breeders in the US and some still exist today. For those interested in the early history of the Merinos, they cannot do better than to read H.B. Carter's excellent book, *His Majesty's Spanish Flock*. Of particular interest to breeders and wool classers will be photographs of the still-preserved samples of wool from several of the rams that came from the continent of Europe between 1720 and 1820. The date of the actual samples is 1791-1803, possibly some came from the rams that were bred in the United Kingdom from stock obtained in Europe. Sir Joseph Banks was in charge of the sheep that made their way to England and apparently he lost no time in trying to devise ways of improving the wool quantity; evidently with some success because the fleece weights of the sheep that eventually arrived in Australia here were about six pounds, already a rise of one sixth on the originals.

Merinos make up the main sheep numbers in Australia and even in wool slumps and bad years they generate a great deal of money for that country. As we have seen, there were in what was to become the United States, breeders of sheep like those in the Angora goat world who were interested in colonizing their country with fine-wool producers. However, there was not apparently the demand for this product. According to H.B. Carter's book, trade patterns unfolding in the last decades of the 18th century showed competition from France for superfine cloths; but the Americans were mainly interested in coarse cloths for the new American States. The combing wool interests of Yorkshire, England, that derived their wool income from the United States almost ceased during the time of the Civil War and caused great hardship among the mill workers in the United Kingdom.

The area where the original Merinos came from in Spain was very hard country and not unlike Australian conditions in many ways. But there was a significant difference, time has proven that Australian soils never carried the actual lime minerals like those in almost all other countries, and many of the difficulties encountered here would have been a direct result of those mineral (both macro and trace) shortfalls. This does not apply to the Americas, where the depth of soil, even if abused, is still far better than would ever be found in Australia.

On the other hand there has always been a difficulty when trying to farm fine wool sheep in a country like England and more fertile parts of Europe because, due to the richness of the soil when compared to the countries of origin, the micron size has increased too much. The same thing occurred when Angora goats were originally introduced to countries where the soils produced fodder with high protein levels; the fineness only lasted a generation or two. Fine wool animals need good mineral levels but *not* high protein and lush conditions. The plains country of New South Wales and Victoria in Australia seemed custom made, as was similar country in South Australia and West Australia.

On August 15, 1884, the first public sale of Merinos in the United Kingdom took place. There are stories of sheep changing hands before then, and possibly the "contraband and doubtful transactions" account for many of those. Suffice it to say that careful breeding even then was starting to produce a steady rise in fleece weights, and obviously some cross breeding with the native English breeds was also taking place. Sir Joseph Banks, the great naturalist, was the moving spirit behind this venture and much of the credit for improvement and indeed the survival of the sheep in the United Kingdom must go to him. MacArthur considered that the wool from the 4th cross was excellent.

As mentioned, H.B. Carter's book is the history of how these closely guarded sheep were obtained from the Spanish and French, and makes fascinating reading. The only sheep known up to that time in the United Kingdom had comparatively coarse wool. This was serviceable for the climate, but not glamourous enough for the clothes of the upper classes. For them the much prized fine wool had to be bought from the continent at great expense, as did the Flemish spinners to process it and teach the English how to do the same. Thus the incentive for this sometimes dubious exercise in importation becomes very apparent. Fortunately for us all the operation was a success. The Merinos created a huge impression when they first arrived in England, although we would be hard put to recognize them today as the progenitors of the many fine specimens nowadays in other parts of the world.

Improvement in the breed appears however to have started before MacArthur obtained his first sheep. Sir Joseph Banks, who was fortunately in charge of the project, had experimented with cross breeding. Possibly he used Lincolns and Leicesters as was done in the antipodes later, and he had already raised the fleece weights quite materially. Good feeding would also have helped in that respect.

Merinos today have two and half times more follicles to the square inch of skin than a cross bred sheep, and possibly the early breeders and farmers of these animals did not realize their high mineral requirements when compared with the other sheep that they had known in their countries of origin. Certainly some of the histories of the early sheep men in Australia have some horrendous descriptions of whole herds being wiped out by footrot; copper is one of the minerals most needed by fine wool sheep, and its absence is the cause of footrot and poor quality wool. Fly-strike, another condition exacerbated by unbalanced soil minerals, particularly magnesium and calcium as well as sulfur and copper, was another enormous scourge. Now we are apparently being faced with a third plague, Johne's disease *(Mycobacterium paratuberculosis)* caused by a bacterium. This disease is completely preventable and curable, if the animal is valuable enough. Bacteria are relatively easy to control. Again we look to mineral shortfalls, copper particularly, and zinc, allied in this instance to very degraded soils.

The accounts of the difficulties experienced by early sheep men in Australia make exhausting and depressing reading. Floods, fires (in abundance) and the various disease conditions seem to have been the norm. In the United States, wolves and coyotes would have caused similar havoc, to say nothing of the ongoing wars between the sheep men and cattle growers.

Meanwhile, the breeders of the humble crossbred sheep who, often quite rightly, considered their sheep far better adapted to the local conditions than the more demanding Merinos, were building up their flocks. Lincolns, Leicesters, Border Leicesters and the bred-up sheep — Polwarths and Corriedales — all emanated in some form or another from Europe and/or the United States and were soon found to be easier to keep, tougher and still produced strong, commercially useful wool and skins. Both Corriedales and Polwarth sheep started to figure in Australia toward the end of the Great War (1914-1918). There are still quite a few Border Leicester breeders with their big raking animals today, many of which have supplied the new sheep milk industry. Cheviots came later, but a few of the early Merino breeders also ran Romneys who seemed to be more resistant to footrot. Like most crossbred sheep, they do not have a copper requirement anywhere near as high as the Merino. This was brought home to me a few years ago when a sheep farmer rang in from Tasmania (an island off southern Australia). It was a wet winter and he had 1,000 sheep in one field — half Merinos and half an English Downs breed. The Merinos were on their hocks and knees the footrot was so bad and the "despised" crossbreeds were in excellent health and no footrot at all. Putting out the lick, which is mentioned later in this book, had the Merinos on their feet in two or three weeks, yet the other sheep hardly touched it — differing copper requirements again.

Wool is an incredible fiber, but it has to contend with the synthetics industry, which is powerful, well organized, and occasionally produces a more durable artifact. When I see photos of modern Chinese cities where practically every male in sight is wearing nylon shirts and probably pants too, where previously another natural material — cotton, was used, one realizes what enormous inroads the synthetics industry has made. The original excuse was that synthetics could be made to look like wool and did not shrink. They are dangerous in fires, however, unlike wool, and not so warm. Modern technology has now produced fine woollen garments of great strength and durability that do not shrink either. The battle is unending, but fortunately so far no one seems to have found a way of making synthetics as warm and safe as wool.

Once we have brought our farm soils up to a reasonable balance and learned to feed the minerals to our sheep that they need, the quality of wool and health of our sheep will improve. The lick already mentioned above and later is made of dolomite, copper sulfate, yellow dusting sulfur and kelp (seaweed meal); the latter is high in zinc. This can be modified to a six-bin feeder with ground limestone and agricultural salt added, and many breeders of all stock prefer to let the animals choose what they need.

The latest world scourges, which are now the flavor of the period, Johne's (Crohn's) disease, are caused by a lack of copper; foot and mouth is caused by herpes rhinovirus and hence a lack of copper and zinc — both will be non-events when these minerals are available as above. BSE and other prion-type diseases are caused by copper in the brain being inhibited. This and more will be discussed later in the book.

This situation has to improve; too many genetics have been lost already in the world, in both the United Kingdom and Australia. De-stocking never was the answer, and never will be for diseases whose origin lies in mineral shortfalls — these are mainly due to bad farming and husbandry.

The methods are much cheaper and more humane than drenches, systemics and preparations for exterior parasites (caused by inadequate sulfur in the system) as well as other modalities hitherto considered indispensable. According to Dr. William Albrecht, sheep that receive the correct amount of copper and other minerals do not get worms or interior parasites of any kind. He was, of course, right. Nowadays when organic certification is a fact of life, this gives us a way of adhering to the rules.

See chapter three for the some of the histories of meat and coarse-wool breeds.

Chapter 3

Breeds of Sheep

Note: I am listing the history that has made some of these sheep; Merinos were accorded space on their own in the last chapter. I am also quoting from the aforementioned *Cyclopedia* of 1900 to list some of the sheep which were to be found in the United States at that time; all apparently sourced from the United Kingdom or Europe. I have no way of knowing how many are still around, a reasonable number I hope; perhaps this book will stir a few memories of their descendants and make growers seek them out or breed back to them. Most were hardy and tough sheep.

Fine Wool

17 microns and below (60s in the old count)

The origins and history of the Merino have been traced in the preceding chapters. In Australia there have been many attempts to bring in other lines such as the Vermonts, but basically the sheep has remained what it was bred up to be, a very fine wool producer indeed. Nowadays the Rambouillets (having migrated in the last century from France to the United States) are much used to maintain the high quality.

The fine wool Merino is used in Sharlee (shedded sheep) setups, and they are looking for a micron count of around fifteen. However, the cost of these seems to have militated against their

Nero (top), Grumpy (bottom) and Cleo (facing page), Sheep from the Second Annual Westray Sale, 1978. Cleo was Grand Champion, strong wool ewe, Sydney Royal Show 1977 with a cut weight of 88 pounds.

widespread adoption, although the number seems to be growing and there are quite a few of these units operating in Australia at present. Most fine-wool to medium-wool Merinos are seen on holdings right across Australia in areas which suit their particular needs.

Strong Wool

Usually above 22 microns (74s to 80s in the old count)

The Corriedale breed is a made-up one using Leicesters, Lincolns and Merinos, the name came from James Little's Corriedale property in North Otago, New Zealand. He used Leicester and Lincoln rams over Merino ewes in pursuit of a dual purpose sheep, producing a fair Corriedale type. The fast maturing fat lambs were all that had been hoped for. In Australia, Davidson and Orbell reversed the method and used Merino rams over Lincoln ewes, thus fixing the Australian Corriedale. The breed society started in 1914, and by 1922 the first flock book was issued with three registered studs.

The Polwarth breed evolved in Australia round 1880 by cross-ing Lincoln rams over Merino ewes and then using a Merino for the comeback. They nearly lost the breed when they introduced the American Vermont (tracing back to the Rambouillet) which produced multiple wrinkles. In Australia fly-strike has always been

Wally Pedericks' prize-winning Corriedale ram and ewe (above and opposite), 1996.

a problem, and when the small, bottle green blowfly arrived it nearly spelled the end for this breed. These flies laid maggots under the wool on any part of the body, not just round the tail and wounds. Devils Grip, an indentation on each side of the shoulder was also another problem that arrived with the Vermonts, and often produced what was called shoulder strike. The problem with this

type of wrinkled skin is that it provides the perfect hiding place for flies to lay their eggs.

The type was eventually fixed as the Polwarth. This, like the Corriedale, did well on richer country. Originally they were known as the Dennis (of Tarndwoorncourt) Comebacks, until the name of Polwarths became official in 1919. Another strain bred by Wettenhalls with Carr's Plains sheep were known as the Ideals or Beau Ideals. These two crosses of the breed known as Carr's Plains and Ideals and Beau Ideals and did well in South America. These were bred by a double cross of Lincoln/Merino rams over Merino ewes. Both strains also virtually became Polwarths.

The object of creating these breeds was to make a strong wool sheep which would be more resistant to footrot, and therefore better on wet country. Of course, these sheep did not have the high copper requirement of the Merino. (No one at that time seems to have been aware that footrot and a lack of copper went together, and that pure Merinos needed more copper than the stronger crossbreeds (see Chapter 2), yet every veterinary book I have seen written up till 1950 was well aware of the fact.)

Dual Purpose Longwools

In the *Cyclopedia* (1900), a farmer from Virginia was quoted as saying: "It is far more profitable to keep different varieties of mutton breeds than the fine-wool Merinos in this part of Virginia." Some of the finest pasture country in the world was and still is to be found in Virginia. It is possible that this land was and remains too rich for Merinos.

In 1900, Leicester sheep justifiably were considered the best sheep of the British breeds. During the 1800s they had been used most successfully for improving the indigenous, long-wool sheep and eventually the Border Leicester was produced. This has been and still is a remarkable dual purpose sheep and was bred for stronger wool and meat. It was used over Merinos in the richer country, and produced a good fat lamb. New Zealanders used Leicesters for producing Corriedales; a breed that is much used these days as a strong and productive dual-purpose sheep.

Other good dual-purpose sheep are:

Carpetmasters — carpet wool sheep bred up from
    Perrindales who have a 'hairy' gene.
Cheviots — a longwool breed from Britain, also used
    for meat. It has a white face and legs.
Cotswolds — a clean-faced English longwool breed
    which was extremely popular in the US.

Australian Romney rams, five years, Keith Jones of Bungaree, Victoria.

Drysdale — carpet wool sheep also crossed with
Merinos earlier on.

Lincoln — another breed with long wool used for carpet
and heavier wool. Also used for breeding up
Corriedales and Polwarths, as above.

Australian Romney — these are descended from the
Romney Marsh English breed. A good type of
meat and coarse wool sheep.

Tukidales — carpet wool.

Meat Breeds

Studs of British breeds became a factor in Australia following
the first successful meat shipment to the United Kingdom in 1880,
and judging by the large number of Downs breeds listed in the
above-mentioned book, in the United States as well. Prior to that
time, few could see a future in meat sheep. After that date the first
freezer ships came into being and it was realized that sheep meat
had considerable export potential. In the United States, the same
will have applied as the meat would have to travel long distances to
service the needs of a country with a large population — far
exceeding anything ever seen in Australia.

Dorset (polled) is an English breed used for fat lambs. This has
the limitation of many polled breeds of stock that it is necessary at
intervals to breed in horned sheep to check a tendency to infertility. The gene for this appears in many polled breeds and if they
become homozygous for it, the progeny will not breed. This also
occurs in polled goats of several breeds.

Dorset (horned) are similar to the polled variety mentioned
above. These are occasionally needed to breed (as above) with
Polled Dorset to stop an infertility factor that can arise on the
polled gene.

Finnish Landrace is a meat breed from Northern Europe, as
the name suggests. Fast growing lambs and leaner meat are the
attraction here. They should cross well with existing meat breeds.
The rams are also early maturing; however, it has been found that
Merinos and several other breeds also have this characteristic when
all the minerals are present in their diet.

Friesian are also known as East Friesian in Australia. It is one
of the more recent imports to Australia, originally via Canada or the

US. These have, of course, come via New Zealand, where they were imported in 1993. They originated in Europe and are characterized by fast maturing lambs, multiple births and good milking ability.

Other meat breeds are:

Hampshires — an English breed, rather similar to Southdowns.

Oxfordshire Downs — bred by crossing a Cotswold ram over a Hampshire Downs ewe.

Perrindales — bred up from a Cheviot/Romney cross. This breed has the reputation in this country for minimal fly-strike incidence, and those I have handled certainly showed this trait.

Ryland — a meat breed from the United Kingdom.

Southdowns — a British breed which were and are renowned as good, fat lamb breeders.

Shropshires — an English breed from the county of that name in the United Kingdom. One hundred years ago these were much prized in the United States.

Suffolk — a black faced and legged meat breed. Here they are also useful at times over cull Merino ewes for a fast growing and easily identifiable meat lamb.

Sussex — an English meat breed.

Texel — these sheep recently arrived in Australia from Denmark and Germany via New Zealand. They were imported into that country in 1986. They are a well-muscled, long-bodied meat sheep, and are believed to have high potential to boost the sheep meat industry.

Natural Wool Shedders

Dorpers are another newly introduced breed of meat sheep that does not need to be shorn and as below should minimize flock work.

The Wiltshire is a horned sheep that sheds its wool and is clean around the breech, so it should not get fly blown. These characteristics hopefully cut flock work to a minimum as the meat is the main object.

Milk Sheep

This is still a fairly young industry in the antipodes and different set-ups are using sheep that suit them. With the possible exception of the East Friesian, no sheep have yet been imported specifically for milking. Both Corriedales and Merinos are being used with success. This is a growth industry which is now well established.

Sheep's milk products, both yogurt and cheese, are a welcome addition to those made from goat's and cow's milk. They both seem to have a more bland flavor than either of the above, so do not need to be sweetened.

At the time of writing, three to four months is reported to be the average length of a lactation. However, I was told that goats did not milk in the winter when I first came here. That was not true either and long lactating lines of sheep will undoubtedly also be found in due course. Even as this edition of the book goes to press, new breeds and genetics are arriving, many via New Zealand from the United States or Canada. The industry has to keep moving to survive.

Below is a list of sheep in the *Cyclopedia*, whose names do not occur above which may or may not still be around. Most countries have Rare Breed trusts nowadays and there are heartening accounts of rescued breeds.

Devonshire Notts — frequently mentioned in this
    book, and their excellence for breeding up is
    emphasized.
Kerry — from Ireland.
Roscommon — also from Ireland.
Somersets
Welsh Mountain

A Note on Fly-strike:
This will be covered further in Chapter 10. Basically, when we came with our family to southern Australia in 1959, our landlords farmed Border Leicesters and Corriedales as well as cattle and

Sheep dog trials.

horses on three farms. Ours was a good-land farm, but like the majority here, the soil pH was low and the calcium and magnesium far below what they should have been. Fly-strike was endemic.

I rode around the 300-acre farm twice a day most days (as soon as I got the children to school and home again). At first, sheep were only struck (by maggots) if they were scouring or had a wound; it was easy enough to bunch them in a corner, tie up the horse and treat the affected part. In 1965 there was a three-year drought which affected a major part of the country. There were mobs of cattle and sheep, many from Queensland, going through on the three chain roads all over Australia for a couple of years. After that we met the green blow-fly as well as the slightly larger brown one that we already had. As mentioned above, they would lay their maggots (not eggs) under the wool.

I would hold the mob in a corner and wait until I saw one of the sheep twitch, on the shoulder, back or whatever, easy to see from a horse. I would tie it up and shear away the wool to find an area, often of 6-12-inches round or more, seething with maggots under what looked like healthy surface wool. It made the job of looking after sheep much more demanding and stressful as sheep could literally be eaten alive.

Chapter 4

Wool and Meat Production

Wool

In Australia the history of fine wool sheep and the production of the best wool has been punctuated by the names of people who at certain times guided the industry in the right direction. In the 1800s it was Thomas Shaw and his son who set the breeders on the rails; his opinion of the breeding skills of the Australian sheep farmers of that era was scathing in the extreme. However, his word prevailed and the Merino began to approach the sort of standard that we expect worldwide today. Even more importantly, he explained the type and presentation of wool to the only processing mills in the world that were handling it at the time in Northern England.

Tom Cully was another such name in the 20th century, born right at its beginning. He taught Graham Holton (acknowledged in his day as the master wool-classer of all Australia) all he knew. Graham told me that as a boy of about 12-years old, between the wars, he cycled out of Sydney to find Tom Cully, determined to make wool his life and learn all that he could. Graham's station, Peak Hill, near Dubbo was a Mecca for wool men, and its annual sales were well known throughout the industry. Graham gave me the pictures of sheep that cut in the region of 40 pounds of wool (which are illustrated in the previous chapter). Many people today feel that 12 pounds is as much as they can hope for in their flocks, in fact a great number of sheep farmers I speak to settle for a much lower weight than that.

There are a great many wool classers in the country today, and on them depends the quality of the clip.

Marketing

There is always a market for the superior article no matter what the industry, but the standard is high and those that do not attain this may have to accept reduced prices for their offerings, which can be used for other purposes. In 2003, as I write this, it looks as though wool — drought notwithstanding — is holding its own if the quality is good.

The production of strong and fine wool always seems to have checkered career. I mentioned in the previous chapters how suited Merino wool of either kind is to blending with cotton, silk, linen and even artificial fibers to produce high quality cloth.

In Australia the Wool Board (the major marketing controller) initially refused to sell wool unless it was to be used on its own, resulting in enormous losses in sales — quite incomprehensible.

Fortunately, commonsense has now prevailed and good wool will now sell for what it is — an excellent fiber peculiarly adapted to mixing with others, both natural and synthetic, as well as being an excellent fiber on its own.

Stocking Rates

In Australia, two to three sheep to the acre should be the top number on a meat concern if good lambs are the object, although these numbers might be modified for U.S. operations. Running too many head does not provide an extra return if the sheep are not getting the feed they need. Depending on the time of sale, it should be remembered that weaners especially have great demands on their systems, and in Australia they take the licks (mentioned later in this book) more than any other single age group. In a dry spring or hard winter, depending on when they are lambed, they will need extra hand feeding as well.

Stocking numbers can affect wool quality quite materially, and it will be found that on farms which excel in wool production, the

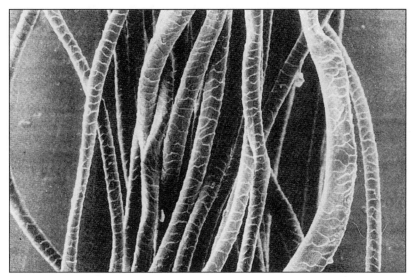

Common wool fiber (from Australian Farm Journal, *November 1993).*

Elite spinners' wool (from Australian Farm Journal, *November 1993).*

numbers may be as low as two sheep to the acre. The bulk weight of the clip will equal or exceed that from a farm running double or triple that number. Perhaps overstocking on land not strong enough to take the numbers is the major downfall of a great many farmers, whatever they carry; as well as contributing materially to land degradation. I work with some sheep grazers out on the central Australian plains where one sheep to ten acres is the norm. As mentioned in the first chapter, sheep improperly farmed have quite disastrous effects on the environment.

Milking stock responds equally to lighter stocking; the average lactation length for milking sheep at present is around four months. During that time and the preceding last two months of pregnancy they should not have to work too hard for their feed. Time was when that was an acceptable lactation length for some goats, and the figure was raised by careful selection — but over-stocking should not figure in any enterprise — even a meat one when figures count. Good quality meat with a reasonable shelf life can only be produced by animals that are well farmed on good land.

Flock Health and the Soil

Nowadays we have another factor called Johne's disease, and this is fortunately avoidable as it is environmental and nutritional. Johne's disease has been with us for many years in every breed of livestock (and humans). During World War II in the United Kingdom, production of foodstuffs had to be maintained and hopefully increased at all costs. This was done by opening up much highly unsuitable land and the heavy use of both phosphatic and nitrogenous artificial fertilizers. A few far-sighted farmers were starting to realize the price of using these modalities, but it was a bit like when Justin von Liebig first "invented" NPK farming in the late 1800s — it was up and running so fast that when he realized his mistake, he could not stop it either. André Voisin, the great French veterinarian and researcher, showed in the 1950s that nitrogenous and phosphatic fertilizers inhibit, or suppress, copper 100 percent. The absence of this mineral in the diets and feed of any animal predisposes it to Johne's disease.

It is unfortunately easier to spread a powder or a spray over the paddock than take the trouble to harrow the manure and spread the necessary lime minerals when their need is indicated (by a soil audit). Dr. Newman Turner, in his great book *Fertility Farming*, first proved that Johne's was not the end of the line and that it was avoidable if the pastures were good enough. The result of the wartime farming was that Johne's disease was endemic in British cattle herds, particularly dairy, but I do not think too many people had tested for it elsewhere. Turner said he remembered vividly seeing his father's cattle being consigned to the abattoirs the moment their scouring became serious, and large numbers ended that way. When he contracted Crohn's disease (the human version of Johne's disease) a year or two later, he wondered wryly why he was not sent the same way.

At present many Merino setups have been de-stocked for this disease. The chapter on soils will point out how this can be avoided by attending to the mineral levels of the fields, as well as avoiding the use of the above-mentioned artificials, and by altering the nutritional status of the flocks.

Feeding

Producing optimum high-quality wool is the goal, whether this is strong wool, fine or ultra fine. This is not as easy as might be imagined, and, in the words of Graham Holton, "It is all in the feeding, no matter how good the breeding, if the feed does not measure up nor does the wool" (or the meat). This does not necessarily mean hand feeding, but getting the soil in top order with all the necessary minerals in the right balance available from the pasture. This should be backed up by the balanced mineral lick (see Chapter 8).

Apart from genetics, good wool depends upon healthy land with a good pH and a correct calcium and magnesium ratio, and especially with adequate copper and sulfur. The chapter on minerals will explain why these are so necessary and also why they are often unobtainable. It will also explain why fly-strike is such a huge problem in Australia, but not so bad in the United States. One U.S. fertilizer consultant in California called me about one of his client's soil analyses and asked if there was anything he should know as he had not met recommendations that did not include "fertilizers" per se before. I said to remember not to spread the trace minerals if the pH (calcium) was below 5.8. He replied that was easy because pH never went below those levels. In the United States perhaps not, here 90 percent of the time it is. He was horrified and asked why we farmed on land like that. I said it is all we have.

One sheep outfit I advise up in the red center of Australia was having a problem in that the sheep were eating the saltbush (an

8-month Corriedale fleece. Melbourne Sheep Show, 1999.

incredible nutritious small shrub very high in minerals that grows in outback areas) faster than it could regenerate. As we drove through the country, it was possible to see how nature was coping with the problem. Nature abhors a vacuum, and in this case a woody shrub called blackbush, which even the kangaroos will not eat, was taking over. Normally, there had been enough saltbush for all. They run one sheep to every ten acres (and one bovine to every twenty). The acreages are enormous and remineralization is virtually impossible. Putting out licks containing the necessary supplementary minerals is the only option, otherwise the stocking rate will have to be reduced still further. If this is done, the sheep will not have to eat so hard to get the necessary minerals and will rest a while each day to chew the cud. It may just save that type of farming.

The amino acids in the gut, particularly cysteine and methionine, cannot work properly unless adequate sulfur is available. Without the amino acids of sulfur, particularly methionine and cysteine, the wool can never reach its full potential and more importantly, selenium cannot be synthesized either. Without copper and sulfur, wool cannot maintain its quality and strength.

Twenty years ago vets in Gippsland (southeast Australia) asked me to find out why so many animals in their practices were selenium deficient when the Department of Agriculture said the mineral was not short in the soil. I sent to the United States for Passwaters' book on selenium, and there it was — without the amino acids of sulfur, selenium could not be assimilated. Every soil analysis we took in Gippsland showed minimal sulfur. It is now known that phosphatic fertilizers tie it up as well as other minerals. It is fashionable to say that discovery of the amino acids of sulfur is fairly recent. An Australian government research organization, CSIR (now known as CSIRO), published a booklet in 1928 listing them all. We keep having to reinvent the wheel.

Feeding for Meat

Compared with fine wool production, breeding sheep for meat presents fewer problems. The essentials are the same: the land must be in good heart, and if there is no overstocking and the sheep's full nutritional needs are met, then the operation should be a success.

All ewes should be given supplementary feed coming up to lambing according to the season, a hard winter after a late autumn break will necessitate hand feeding barley with 10 percent lupin for crossbred sheep and additional hay should bring them up to lambing in good order. As many of them will almost certainly be feeding twins or even higher numbers, it must be remembered that they will need almost twice the amount required by a ewe with a single lamb.

Remember meat lambs are grown on their mothers' milk, and if it is poor quality due to lack of minerals and inadequate feed when in-lamb, they are not going to do very well.

Feeding for Wool

One hundred years ago, according the *Cyclopedia* already mentioned, the average yield for wool in the United States was five pounds, one more pound than in Australia at the same time. Part of the above applies, particularly the advice about not feeding high protein. Those who run Sharlee know that it is the carbohydrates and the minerals that need to be maintained. I have mentioned elsewhere the failure of farmers in the United Kingdom to produce fine wool, not just on sheep but on angoras and possibly even alpacas (we shall find out on that one).

Merinos can take 20 to 30 percent lupin in the same mix. Even in a good winter some extra feeding will pay dividends. The lambs are fattened from the ewes milk; this depends largely on the caliber of the prenatal feeding, which determines both the quantity and quality of the ewe's milk.

As mentioned earlier, Merinos have 2.5 times the amount of wool-bearing follicles per square inch compared with meat sheep, this means a far larger copper requirement to grow the fleece, let alone maintain the health of the animal. In the meat breeds twinning is the norm, and it is often the overlarge single lamb that causes birthing troubles. A lack of potassium in the pastures leads to lamb pulling (at birthing time) on a large scale. This deficiency can arise in prolonged drought where there is no green feed obtainable, or it can be the result of overzealous use of artificial fertilizers. It is more commonly the latter. Using unpasteurized cider vinegar sprayed onto hay twice a week coming up to lambing can offset this unfortunate phenomenon.

Feeding for Milk

Remember that it is not high protein that increases milk production, but a supply of good carbohydrates. When I milked goats commercially, others in the same game used to review my feeding regime and wonder how on earth I achieved higher figures than they did. When, in desperation, they had to cut back the high protein in their feeds, usually due to ill health in their herds, they found to their amazement that the milk went up, not down, and the quality was better.

One fact should be remembered: the higher the protein in the diet the greater the need for copper, which explains why the rather startling amount of copper that Graham Holton told me he used did not cause trouble as his sheep were fed to the hilt for high fleece weights. This phenomenon is noticeable in the United Kingdom right across the board; their dairy animals need more copper than ours would ever need here. A dairyman in the United Kingdom feeds 80 grams per head of the stock lick to his cows with highly beneficial results. I had advised him that 40 to 60 grams would be more than adequate.

Grain Feeding — The Merits of Barley

Many years ago I read an old farming book (Baïracli-Levy) that reckoned barley was the best grain for all stock, although I do not think the exact reason was known at that time. Work done with pigs in the United Kingdom highlighted the fact that this is a very useful grain. When pigs were fed maize and other grains they became unthrifty to the point of death; they were actually dying of necrotic enteritis. This happens when there is a lack of vitamin B5 (pantothenic acid) which is found in barley. As soon as barley was added to the ration, this effect ceased and the animals recovered. As far as I know this applies right across the board.

In the early days not much was known about that particular B vitamin (or many others). Without B5 a sheep (or any animal) cannot make its own cortisone in the adrenal cortex. Vitamin C and vitamin B5 are needed for this process and all animals (with certain exceptions, see section on vitamin C) synthesize vitamin C in their livers from their feed.

Multiple Births

Twinning may, of course, not be a genetic trait, it could be environmental as the copper intake is crucial in lambing percentages. Graham Holton told me he expects 120 percent lambs from his Merinos. So far the general percentage mentioned in Merinos is about 85 percent at the top of the scale and well below that in less well-managed flocks. A farmer whose Merinos have been on dolomite licks with the added copper, sulphur and seaweed for a year has already raised his percentages to 95 percent from about 65 percent. Meat sheep have a much lower copper requirement as they do not carry large amounts of wool and have, therefore, a rather unjustified reputation for being hardier. They will, however, need some copper and sulfur. The latter mineral, as mentioned, is needed for optimum food conversion.

Any ewe feeding twins will need at least half again as much feed as one nursing a single lamb, if the lambs are to grow properly. If the farm has been remineralized and is run on sound natural lines, they should all do very well. Spring dropped lambs definitely do better growth-wise, as it is the natural time for all young to be born. Growth rates are never as high at other times of year (nor is milk production).

Stock Lick

The lick mentioned below and in Chapter 8 must be available at all times as the dolomite helps prevent mastitis, a most uneconomical complaint in sheep, because it is usually too late when the farmer finds out that a ewe is afflicted. On concerns where the size of the acreage precludes land improvement, this lick is even more necessary. On farms where soil analysis and top-dressing to balance the lime minerals and gypsum can be carried out, the resultant improvement both in performance and health will make the exercise worthwhile. But even on these farms it pays to have the lick out all the time as seasonal variations can effect mineral availability.

A farmer who rang me in January 1993 started to put licks out for his sheep shortly after. We worked the licks out from what was missing in the analysis of his farm. The pH was low, calcium, magnesium and sulfur were greatly out of balance and in short supply. Copper was extremely low as were cobalt and zinc. The licks consisted of:

25 kg (55 pounds) dolomite,
4 kg (9 pounds) copper sulfate (see note below)

4 kg (9 pounds) fine yellow sufur
4 kg (9 pounds) seaweed meal

Half a kilogram (one pound) of cobalt could have been included if cobalt deficiency problems warranted it. On the sway back belt of South Australia farmers tell me they add one kg (2.2 pounds) of cobalt sulfate to their licks with great success. I was doing a talk over there in the spring of 1998 when I was told of this. I should have been hesitant to mention such a large amount, but it is very satisfactory when graziers work these things out for themselves.

Similarly 250 grams of Borax (sodium borate) can be added if the boron levels are too low. This is particularly important if the flock contains sheep which are up in years and therefore more prone to arthritis, which is linked to lack of that mineral. It would also help in keeping the teeth firm in the jaw, as long as the wear is even it should not be necessary to dress the teeth with an angle grinder periodically as often used to be done.

This is a loose mix *dry* lick, and nothing else should be added except possibly some grain on the top to start the sheep taking it. On *no* account should molasses be added. Reports from the United States and Europe suggest that flies like to strike animals that have sugar in their blood. Nowadays this should be avoided at all costs; both Ross River fever and Anthrax are spread by biting insects. The seaweed in the lick takes care of the other trace minerals, including boron, cobalt, selenium and iodine (which is not strictly speaking a mineral).

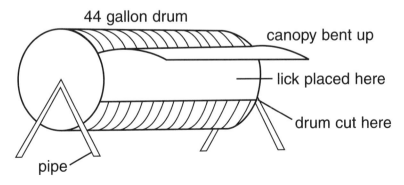

A lick feeder that is cheap and easy to make.

Subsequent work I did with stock both here and in the United Kingdom since this book was first produced has highlighted the fact that the less processed and the more basic the minerals and seaweed are, the better the assimilation. Chelated minerals by mouth are a definite no-no, and must be avoided at all costs; they upset the animals in the case I saw to the point of death (by causing liver damage) as well as being extremely expensive.

Results

A farmer rang me and said he had poor lambing percentages, tender wool, a short staple with average fleece weight of about five pounds after 12 months. The lick was put out soon after the call. He rang me about 10 months later to say that he had just sheared at nine months, the fleece weights were 11 pounds, the staple was 1.5-inches longer than the previous shearing and there was no tender wool, the clip was the best he had shorn for about 15 years. He also reported a marked fall in fly-strike during what had been an extremely bad summer for that complaint — he had about 2-3 percent while those around him were talking well into high double figures. The next step of course will be to bring at least some of his large acreage into line, so that the lick will be a standby for bad times, not a necessity for the whole year. However, on this score I advise farmers to keep licks out 365 days as the sheep will know far quicker than the grazier when they need them, so access should really be all the year round.

It is important that licks are kept weather proof, one inch of rain on the lick will neutralize the copper (and cobalt if it has been included) so it disappears in about half an hour. Presumably the dolomite sets up a chemical reaction which causes this to occur. Sheep and other stock mainly seem to take the licks because they feel they need the copper. The whole exercise will be wasted if the licks are allowed to get wet. It is fairly easy to construct rainproof lick containers for sheep as they are not as destructive as cattle. The drawing on page 35 is of a simple lick container which a farmer on Kangaroo Island thought out. (See note in previous chapter on having all the ingredients out separately.)

There is no doubt that the finer the wool the greater is the need for copper in the diet. Another factor that influences this has already been mentioned — high protein. This explains something that I had wondered about, and that is the high levels of copper fed to some Merinos in top production with apparently no ill effects at all.

Meat Sheep

Meat sheep do not need so much copper as the heavy wool bearers. Corriedale's and Polwarth's needs are not as high as Merino's but they are still greater than the meat breeds. The extra follicles per square inch found in Merinos, and to a point in their crosses, make for a high dietary requirement of the mineral.

In the lick above we are beginning to consider feeding all the items as mentioned; then the British breeds can take as much or as little as they need of copper. We found that they generally take less than the high producing wool breeds. See the sections on copper and sulfur for the disease and health conditions *avoided* by making sure both are in adequate supply.

Shedded Sheep

Shedded sheep are known as Sharlee in Australia. This is a process of shedding Merinos with superfine or top quality wool. It has also been attempted with cashmere goats and I will be interested to see how it goes as goats historically are healthier when they are allowed plenty of exercise. Nowadays Sharlee wool needs to be finer than 15.5 microns to be an economic proposition.

I have helped several Sharlee concerns to set up and keep their sheep healthy over the years. The rules are of course the same: make sure that the fodder used is properly grown on remineralized soil. One of the more successful outfits grows grain hay and feeds it chopped in fairly large self help hoppers. The lick already mentioned has either to be available or should be fed in amount of about four to five grams per head per day, depending on the age of the Merinos. Make sure the best source of water possible is used, *not* reticulated town water, either water from a good bore (have it tested) or rainwater would be quite suitable.

It seems that the more room the sheep have to move around, the healthier they are and ideally some green food (not alfalfa) would probably help. High protein feeds and fine wool production do not go together and this is one of the main reasons why fine

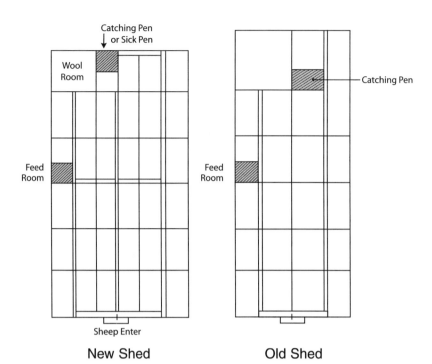

Catching Pen
or Sick Pen

Wool
Room

Catching Pen

Feed
Room

Feed
Room

Sheep Enter

New Shed   Old Shed

Plans of the old shed and the new shed of a Sharlee operation in northeastern Victoria.

The old Sharlee shed with new sheep, 1991.

The new Sharlee shed, 1999.

fleece animals — be they angoras, alpacas or fine wool sheep — have never been a success in countries where the soils are very rich.

The setting up and running of such an enterprise is expensive but obviously worth it in the higher payment for the clip. Again the success or failure both financially and in fact lies in feeding and managing them economically enough to keep the sheep in top order and producing the best fleeces.

The farmers that I advise all buy in their sheep so do not breed any for their own purpose, again I presume that makes sense financially. It would certainly pay to grow their own remineralized fodder; at present most of them buy in what they can get. The outfit which so kindly made the information below available is chaffing round bales of oaten hay as the main feed which seems a good idea and even better if he could guarantee how the hay was grown.

Reproduced here are plans and photos of a Sharlee operation in north central Victoria, Australia. The owner of this shed had the misfortune to lose his first one by fire and has built this with hindsight hoping to have ironed out one or two details that were not as good as he liked in the first shed. He has tried to make the feeders less wasteful and also to prevent vegetable matter from the feed getting into the fleeces.

The shed has nearly three yards clearance, which means that small tractors and machinery used to keep it clean underneath have plenty of room to operate. The floor is half inch reinforcing mesh covered by one-inch-by-one-inch galvanized mesh. In the previous shed he had wooden floors and now finds that the sheep's feet are in much better condition without the wood which would require daily cleaning to be practicable; even then the life span of the wood is only three to four years.

The sheep are fed once a day only with chopped oaten hay, which we hope eventually will be grown on the place. Vitamins and minerals are fed every second day on a self help basis. Water troughs are two feet above floor level which stops fouling with manure, but the occasional bit of straw gets in. PVC pipe with holes cut in it for water are occasionally used, but are not a apparently a success because the water gets fouled too quickly. Clean water is paramount.

Pen sizes are 20 feet by 7 feet and each pen holds 17 sheep. This very wisely allows for three extra feeding spaces for shy sheep to make sure they all feed at once.

New sheep coming in are weighed and after a couple or three months they are separated out according to weight. The farmer has found that feeding all identically does not necessarily mean identical growth and genetic differences would account for this. Unless he ever reaches the stage (unlikely as it would not be economic) of growing all his own sheep this factor should remain the same.

The average cost of the rugs over the five sizes required is about five dollars (US) per sheep or slightly less. The average cost of keeping a sheep shedded is around 35 dollars a year, this is of course variable according to fodder costs, insurance, rugs, maintenance, etc.

In both the old shed and the new one shown, the feed room is in the center. The wool room in the new one is sunken and this allows a raised shearing board which makes for easier handling. In Australia the Sharlee Ultra Fine Society have a starter kit for anyone thinking of setting up a Sharlee system. This covers layout, sheep selection, nutrition, economics, preparing sheep for shedding and shed management. It also has a section on preparing the Sharlee Wool Clip. The cost of this publication is available and includes one-year subscription to the society from the Sharlee Society, Royal Showgrounds, Epsom Rd, Ascot Vale, Victoria 3032, Australia.

Chapter 5

Feeding Requirements

When lambing and feeding the in-lamb ewes, whatever the breed, if the pastures are balanced mineral-wise, extra feed for lambs should not be necessary providing rainfall has been adequate. Even so, a mineral lick containing the essentials is always a good idea at any time and on any farm. But if the land has not been brought up to the correct mineral balance, supplementary feeding for the ewes will be necessary both during pregnancy and until the lambs are weaned. It is important that they have a continuous supply of good pasture. Analyze the land as suggested to find out what minerals are out of balance or missing.

Quite a few farmers I know have changed over to spring lambing now; the old deterrent to this in Australia particularly, was tender wool and wool-break. These conditions are due entirely to the fact that there were not enough of the necessary minerals in the feed (whether animals were hand or pasture fed) to maintain both the ewe and the fetus up to lambing. When the correct minerals are provided in the lick or feed year round this problem does not occur. The old early autumn lambing where the lambs had to soldier on through an often harsh winter while ewes tried to provide enough milk on winter feed to keep them healthy was hard on the ewes' systems as well as the lambs' growth rates. That is one of the reasons that so many elderly ewes in Australia have such bad mouths. Their health suffers in the lambing process as they cannot get the nutrients to maintain themselves, particularly their teeth, and the lambs. In the colder parts of Europe and the United States it can also be hard on the lambs trying to get a start without any green grass through the often very cold winter.

Spring lambing means that the lambs are arriving as the pasture comes into its best — the natural time for all species to be born. There is little doubt that lambs born at this time of year tend to be inherently tougher. After a few years on this program most sheep farmers are impressed with the lambs' growth and health.

Supplementary winter feeding and the provision of the lick mentioned in the last chapter will be needed for both autumn and spring lambing. The health of the patures and the weather pattern will be the crucial factors. With late autumn lambing, feed and minerals may be needed to keep the ewes in milk during a harsh winter especially if there is a drought — a fairly regular occurrence — not just in Australia. For spring lambing, the minerals are needed to ensure that the ewes will have enough milk to carry the lambs through possible dry spells in good condition coming up to weaning. The ewes also have to maintain their own condition coming into summer. The stress of poor feed quality at certain times affects the wool and body score and these factors are minimized or completely avoided if the correct minerals are available at all times.

The Australian system of never hand feeding young sheep can cause trouble because in very bad seasons the sheep must then be taught to take what is given to them if they are to stay alive. I found it took two months to train some old Merino ewes that licks and hay were to be freely taken — once they got the message they were fine. If the ewes do not know what hay and licks are initially, and this may happen if they have never been hand fed, sprinkle some lupins or barley on the top of hay to start them off. The ideal of course is to make sure that all lambs are taught at weaning, marking (castrating) and mulesing time, if not before. (Mulesing is a practice, largely used in Australia, where a portion of the skin is removed from around the tail and anus to prevent fly-strike.) They need to learn that food can come in troughs as well as growing in the fields. This will not be a problem in the United States, as, according to the region, the climate dictates that all sheep learn to eat brought in fodder fairly early in their lives.

In dairying there used to be a significant number of farmers who did not think it necessary to feed dry (pregnant) cows/does (goats) or sheep coming up to parturition; invariably the milk supply was well below what it should have been and the dams lost condition while milking. If the ewes are fed on a slightly rising plane of nutrition, especially mineral-wise in the last two months of pregnancy, they should come through in good fettle. Remember that "pulling" (manual assistance at birth) lambs is caused by a lack of potassium, this can be supplied by watering diluted cider vinegar onto hay at a rate of about 50 ml per ewe twice a week for the last five weeks before lambing, or it can be added to the seaweed/cod-liver oil pre-lambing drench.

In particularly hard conditions, barley with 10 percent lupins for meat sheep (crossbreeds), or barley with 25 percent lupins for Merinos, cuts out the often inevitable decrease in the wool (and milk) quality during those times. Work that has come to hand in recent times suggests that barley is the better grain and should be used as the major part of the ration. Vitamin B5 (see Chapter 9) is provided by this grain. Juliette de Baïracli-Levy, the great Israeli herbalist and authority on animal health in the early part of the 20th Century, emphasizes the advantage of barley over all other grains. Probably neither she nor anyone else knew the exact mechanics in those days.

This "discovery" was made in the pig industry in the United Kingdom a few years ago when pigs fed maize and other grains were dying from what looked like necrotic enteritis; the vets were right on the ball and diagnosed it as a condition caused by a deficiency of vitamin B5. This condition ceased as soon as the barley was added to the ration. Prior to that, maize (corn), which supplies adequate vitamin B6 only, was fed on its own in those operations. The barley and maize were fed half in half and the trouble ceased. As mentioned in the last chapter this vitamin is needed for cortisone production in the body (along with vitamin C) and is absolutely essential.

Liquid kelp (urea free) is now readily available and is an excellent drench at this time if the ewes appear to be in low condition (give about six to eight ml each). Make sure kelp is as nature has intended and has no chelated minerals added; these are not desirable by mouth, but as has been pointed out by Dr. Ed McDonough in *Acres U.S.A.*, it is brilliant for EDTA chelation (in the blood) in humans, but not for sheep. Fed by mouth chelated minerals go straight to the liver and ultimately cause death. Those who have read *Natural Cattle Care* will know the story of how I was confronted with 300 Friesian Holstein cattle literally dying on their feet. I found out that their mineral mix — costing 1,000 pounds sterling a month (approximately $1,730) — was made of almost entirely chelated minerals. They were put onto 80 grams per day of the lick already mentioned in Chapter 4 (and again in Chapter 8) and they started to recover in four days.

Seaweed (kelp) either as a powder or a liquid will guard against pregnancy toxemia, also called twin lamb disease. This is not a disease at all, but a condition where the lambs have taken what minerals they needed from the dam and she has not enough left to live on. Kelp, being natural, gives the quickest and most effectual boost. There was a classic example of this some years ago when Australian shipments of meat sheep to the Arabian nations nearly came to a halt. They were dying two weeks out, and tests showed they were lacking in zinc and potassium. This was promptly added to the next lot of pellets, but the deaths continued. A senior vet in the University of Sydney told them to add kelp instead of zinc and potassium. The deaths stopped at once; because even though on paper they were getting far less potassium and zinc than that which had been added to the pellets, minerals in their natural state work far more effectively than artificial ones. As mentioned earlier, if some cod-liver oil is added to the pre-lambing drench where necessary, it will work even better. Check the sections on vitamins A and D in Chapter 8.

For reasons mentioned above, farmers should consider seriously breeding the ewes and rams so that the ewes do lamb down in spring according to which part of the United States they are situated. From every point of view it is more desirable.

When the pastures are balanced, a supply of good quality supplementary hay with licks available is all that is needed if there is a drought. Do not forget that Merinos, to be fully healthy need nearly as many minerals in their feed as goats, those two and one-half times the extra follicles to the square inch mean a large drain on the system (especially of copper) which crossbreed (meat breeds) sheep will not experience to the same degree.

All these remarks apply equally to milk sheep; which will of course be lambed down according to the milk schedule. If they are brought through pregnancy in good condition, both the milk supply and the lambs will benefit.

Lambs

Provided the pastures are not deficient in potassium, all the lambs should arrive without trauma, which only arises if that mineral is lacking. As long as the ewes have had extra cider vinegar on their feed or in drinking water (if watered from troughs), they should have a trouble-free lambing. Dystokia (difficult lambing) is caused by low potassium in the field pasture (usually caused by too much NPK farming) and letting the land become degraded. Blood vessel constriction in small veins occurs when potassium is low — as in RSI (repetitive stress injury) in humans and navicular disease in horses. When potassium is low, the blood supply to the fetus, uterus and cervix is limited to the point where it (they) cannot move about *in utero* as they should at a time when it is most necessary for their well being. If all is well a normal birth and presentation, accompanied by the uterine contractions, will ensure everything takes place as it should.

An easy way of feeding cider vinegar is to spray it onto hay or grain. For example, a roller bale can be unrolled and about 10 liters of cider vinegar in about 100 liters of water can be sprayed onto the hay. This method has been used by many farmers and works well. The rate is about three to four ml per head per week, for the last three weeks before lambing.

If the land is conventionally farmed with NPK fertilizers and has not been remineralized, all the above problems will be more frequent. In addition to the minerals mentioned above, vitamins A and D must be supplied as well and cod-liver oil, if feasible, is the best source. This will ensure the lambs are not born with contracted tendons (knuckle over) and that they will have enough vitamin A and D to carry them through. If these vitamins are low, due to drought or other factors, lambs will die at or before nine days old. Vitamins A and D can be given by injection, but may cause a mess at the injection site in wool-bearing animals. Both potassium and vitamins A and D are inhibited by the use of conventional fertilizers, as are all minerals and vitamins, up to 28.5 percent less of both are available (research reported by Widdowson as carried out in the Haughley Experiment).

Cobalt deficiency generally only affects lambs in their first year, they obviously have a great requirement during that time. Farmers tell me that by the time the sheep are four-years old they are all well grown, and seem to have caught up any stunting that occurred in their first year. The fact remains that shortfalls must be avoided, no animal can produce a decent fleece while trying to catch up on a bad mineral shortfall. Cobalt can easily be monitored on a soil analysis, and with sheep it is essential to know if there is a shortfall. On what is known as the "swayback belt" in South Australia farmers add two pounds of cobalt sulfate to the lick. This is enough to stop dying and wasting in the lambs.

The lambs' first necessary contact with the farmer will be at marking (castrating and cutting off the tails) and possibly mulesing (generally on Merinos) if the latter has to be carried out. On farms where cobalt levels are not very good, an injection of high-potency vitamin B12 when the lambs are handled at this time would be a good idea. If the levels are very low, see above. Cobalt is a highly toxic mineral and must not exceed a teaspoon (three grams) between 40 sheep per day and is best fed watered in a diluted state onto feed or in water. When it is added to the lick, sheep will only take what they need. Consult your vet as to the best methods of supplementation.

Polyarthritis, also called infectious arthritis, is covered in Chapter 10 but needs mentioning here as well. Outbreaks of arthritis after mulesing are often reported. This would be polyarthritis, similar to that contracted through the navel cord and is generally caused by corynebacteria, a particularly intransigent germ. Some (not all) farmers tell me that once the lamb has been marked, docked and mulesed, it is just dropped onto the ground with the raw flesh landing on the contaminated soil in the handling yard. Generally the same yards are used year after year. In the old days in the Northern Hemisphere, sheep marking yards were moved each year and I believe this is done in South Africa. These yards were usually made of wattle hurdles or similar light material. If the yards cannot be moved, a very heavy lime application in the marking yard would be a good idea between operations.

Dropping the newly marked and mulesed lamb on the ground seems a highly unnecessary and unhygienic practice. A bed of wool soaked in disinfectant onto which the lamb could be allowed to land would go some way to ensuring it did not pick up the infective organisms (corynebacteria) at this time. Of course putting the lamb down on its feet would help too, and would not really take that much longer, many farmers tell me they do this as a matter of course. Another practice that should always be considered if portable yards are used is never to use the same stretch of ground twice for this job (see above). Corynebacteria, which also can cause Caseous Lymphadenitis (CLA, or cheesy gland), lurks in the soil of old yards. Angora farmers in South Africa found that the only way to break the CLA cycle was to make fresh yards each year. They reported that the vaccines were no substitute for good management and this holds good right across the board.

Weaners

Farmers constantly remark to me when they put out licks as advised in this book, to whatever kind of stock, that the weaners and young growing beasts take by far the greatest amount. This after all hardly is surprising when one considers that they (in the case of weaners) have just left their dams and are also increasing in size at a great rate. Once they reach maturity the demands on their systems are not so high. Therefore it is quite essential that licks are available during these first months, even when the pastures have been remineralized. When farmers are bringing their depleted land back into line, I always suggest that they do at least one field properly and gradually work across the farm as finances permit. On some holdings it is impractical to do it all at once.

On very large farms and ranches it is only economic to do a paddock or two by the homestead or sheds. This means that there will always be a really good field available to put the ewes in prior to lambing and again for the weaners when they come off the ewes — the rams will benefit from it coming up to joining, too. If this is not possible, provision will have to be made to see that the weaners get some extra hay if necessary, the minerals they need can be spread on this, which is quite easy if the hay is in round bales. But if the lick mentioned above is out and they are taking it, that should be all that is necessary.

A farm that has not been and probably never will be remineralized due to its great area has used the lick I describe in this book for many years. The first year of using it they got top weaner clip of the state of Victoria. My daughter, who is a wool classer, brought me a sample of the wool to see and it was excellent.

Rams

These, in spite of their comparatively short working season, need to be kept healthy during the rest of the year. It is no good leaving them in a scrubby, unbalanced field all the year round and expect them to work really hard with no back-up when joining time comes. All rams should be on a rising plane of nutrition for three months coming up to joining, whatever time of year that is. If the change to spring lambing is contemplated, they will have to be hand fed with their minerals and grain should it be a dry summer.

Rams in dry conditions with no green feed *must* be supplemented with vitamins A and D, otherwise they may go infertile due to a lack of vitamin A and this kind of infertility is irreversible. In a ewe this deficiency will cause temporary infertility, but it is permanent in a ram. An injection of high potency A, D and E several times during the late spring, summer and autumn will bring them all through safely, or they can be given about 10 ml of cod-liver oil orally, once a fortnight should be enough, or it can be mixed into the grain ration if it is eaten immediately. It must be remembered that vitamins are destroyed by light, therefore if fed in this manner the fodder must be eaten straight away.

This is where the improved, remineralized field mentioned above can be used to run the rams in coming up to joining. Fields that have been top-dressed with phosphatic or nitrogenous fertilizers will be dangerously low in many minerals and vitamins, especially copper and vitamins A and D. Both urea and phosphatic fertilizers inhibit minerals and vitamins.

It would also be a good idea to give all rams a drench with liquid seaweed, six to eight ml at regular intervals during the summer as this would ensure that their sperm was as good as possible. A lack of selenium (which is contained in seaweed) is a contributing factor in weak sperm of poor quality. The lick listed in the last chapter, which contains powdered seaweed, should also be available at all times. The sulfur in the lick is incredibly important for the males, without the amino acids of sulfur, particularly methionine and cysteine, selenium cannot be absorbed as it should.

Hay and possibly a small quantity of lupins and oats or barley in the ratio of one part lupins to 10 parts barley if conditions are extra hard, make a good ration. Lupins should not be fed in greater amounts than this, they deplete iodine in the system which can lead to many metabolic disorders. Remember that in any year and in any country the autumn is always the danger period. This is when the nutrients in the dying off spring/summer feed are at their lowest level, and the situation will not improve at all until the autumn or late summer rains. Even after that the licks should be kept out as the new growth will not contain any minerals for the first six weeks.

Ewes

These are doing a double job, producing lambs as well as (hopefully) a decent quality fleece and or milk in dairying set-ups, and should be fed accordingly. Their nutrition must be attended to prior to joining and in the last two months of pregnancy. I am often quite aghast at the lambing percentages that a lot of farmers take for granted. A while ago a Merino breeder told me quite calmly that his were about 30 percent. He did not know where the shortfall was occurring.

Ewes that do not cycle when they should are deficient in copper. If they cycle, are covered, and do not hold they are low in vitamins A and D (or the rams are infertile). It may be good practice to give the ewes an injection or oral dose of cod-liver oil (vitamin A and D) at the same time that the rams receive their last dose. If the ewes slip their lambs or abort it is generally due to a lack of those vitamins — vitamin A in particular.

Twin lamb disease, which of course is not a disease at all — it merely means the ewe has run out of essential minerals because the lambs have taken what they need, so nothing is left for her and she collapses — is easily averted if the diet is right. As mentioned above, liquid seaweed drench is invaluable at this stage. At the slightest sign of unhappiness in the ewes it is wise to give all of them five to seven ml of the liquid by drench. Cases that go down should have it every day until they recover; usually two doses are enough, but this should not occur if the pastures are improved and the licks are available.

All these methods are to a point Band-Aids — it is obviously easier to have the conditions right (weather permitting) on an improved farm run along organic lines, which will mean that most of the right amount of minerals and vitamins are available from the pasture. Licks would act as a backup in those circumstances, not an absolute necessity.

At shearing time a close examination of the wool will show the times when the ewes were under nutritional stress, a quite clear break will be seen. Sometimes it is bad enough for the wool to look as though is has been cut. This kind of stress is caused by inadequate copper and sulfur, allied to poor feed. They are the two minerals considered most important for wool quality.

Wethers

These are usually expected to maintain themselves on rather ordinary pasture. They are, after all, only providing the farmer with a (hopefully) good quality fleece each year. Again, they can only produce a fleece as good as their genetics and the condition of the farm allows. It is quite essential that they receive licks containing dolomite, copper, sulfur and seaweed as suggested. Farmers here tell me that sheath-rot (pizzle-rot) and fly-strike are minimal to non-existent when sheep are getting the licks. Both are usually a menace for wethers. A farmer who had put licks out in the spring of 1993 because of fly-strike problems rang me in amazement the week after the licks were put out. Quite obviously the flies had struck, but the maggots had not burrowed in at all, and the lesions had dried up. One wether had been struck the day before across the back, the maggots were all dropping off the belly wool. Evidently the correct amount of sulfur and other minerals in the sheep's systems made them quite unpalatable. Due to the better soils in the United States, many of these problems will not arise; however, it is best to know what to do if the time does come. I felt this when I prepared my book, *Natural Horse Care,* for publication in the United States, and then was amazed when the calls started to come in with exactly the same problems that we have here.

Licks

This is really a grey area. Some farmers tell me that sheep take them immediately without any trouble, others say that their sheep take a long time to come onto them. Technically sheep will take a lick if they need it, but it does seem that those that have never been hand fed or seen a lick container may take up to two months to go to a lick. Running a couple of Merino ewes, which my daughter had been given as they were damaged by polyarthritis when young, to keep my new garden under some kind of control was an interesting project. Obviously they came from a fairly rough farm or they would not have been infected when young and just as obviously they had never been hand fed. They patently needed supplements and were in poor condition, my daughter had saved them from starving, but they totally ignored anything I put out. I made the breakthrough with hay, on which I would spread a little of the base lick, then they started to get the message and eventually got to the stage where they waited outside the back door for me to appear, but it took two months. Obviously farmers who never hand feed their stock must be fairly rare. Some have found that putting some grain on the top of the lick will start the sheep off, or it can be spread on hay as I did initially.

As mentioned above minerals are, of course, unavailable during prolonged drought as well and drought does happen in the United States. When the rain does come, too often farmers think that because some feed is starting to show up that all their problems are solved. I have seen farmers stop hand feeding from the day pasture starts growing with, of course, disastrous results. See the end of this chapter for alternative ways of feeding minerals.

Salt

This should be given separately because the sheep's need for it may vary and the minerals in the lick should be taken because they are needed not because of the salt content. Salt is needed on some farms and it is better to let the sheep take it free choice. If they go mad for salt, suspect a potassium shortfall, as the two interact. One of my farmers rang me because his sheep were eating salt by the pound, which eventually would have killed them. I suggested he put out some hay and spray it with cider vinegar (in water), this he did and they stopped eating the salt at once. This happened on a very poor farm and should this occur make sure that cider vinegar (for the potassium) is made available occasionally. Also take steps to improve the potassium-deficient pastures.

Prolonged drought can produce this effect. Potassium comes from green feed grown *without* artificials.

When I was talking at a meeting of the Biological Farmers of Australia (an organic body) some years ago, one farmer said that he considered molasses and salt were "lollies" for sheep and should not be put in licks. I agree. Molasses is only indicated for an animal that uses its muscles and is not really necessary then (vitamin C works equally well without the undesirable side effects). Nowadays with three extremely nasty diseases that are carried by flies: Anthrax, Ross River Fever and EIA (Equine Infectious Anaemia or horse AIDS), molasses, which encourages biting insects, should never be used. Research done in the States and reports in *Acres U.S.A.* indicate that stock with sugar in their veins are very palatable to flies. Molasses, like sugar, also interferes with the laying down of calcium (and magnesium).

Proprietary Licks

Unfortunately, most proprietary licks contain far too much sodium and not enough of the necessary minerals like magnesium, calcium, sulfur, etc. It is cheaper to put out one's own lick and tailor it to the analysis where necessary. Extra cobalt and boron are the two most usual additions.

Goitrogenic Feeds

All legumes including tagasaste (see next chapter) come into this category. In Australia, tagasaste is also called lucerne, in the States it is known as alfalfa. Goitrogenic means that fed in excess these plants cause iodine depletion. The name arises because this condition usually causes the goiter to swell, an affect which would not be noticed in sheep (read the section on iodine in Chapter 8). At school we were taught that all zygomorphic flowered plants, such as beans and peas, came into this category.

Legumes include all clovers, soy and ordinary beans, lupins, peas, alfalfa and lucerne trees (as well as the Australian tagasaste). First-cut dryland alfalfa whose roots go down to 14 feet or more, according to some reports, is obviously a safe feed because it is mixed with grass. Nor is it top dressed with superphosphate or irrigated (hopefully). However having the above stock lick out when sheep are on dryland alfalfa would still be a good idea, just in case the iodine should get low. I work with farmers on dryland alfalfa and saltbush country and all report that the licks are a useful adjunct to the diet.

Irrigation alfalfa may look very nice, but if fed as hay it has been found to be extremely dangerous on occasion. I can only assume that because several cuts a year are forced off the land it has to be grown with artificial help. It is also irrigated, so the roots do not go down for their nutrients and water, but merely wait near the top of the soil waiting for the next hit of water and fertilizer. It is incredibly goitrogenic and has quite often caused multiple problems in all stock.

When iodine is depleted the adrenals, and thus all other glands, cease to work properly and it will mean general ill health all round. Ewe lambs, if conceived, will be born weak and dying and possibly without wool, on the other hand, the ram lambs will be alright as the male requirement for iodine is not so high as the females.

The bottom (and top) line to this chapter is make sure that all the sheep have access to the lick already mentioned several times for 365 days a year. European farmers of all stock are great on this and have feed and lick containers which can be towed from each field to the next to follow the stock around. Of course in the colder climates they are brought into the barns and yards where the animals are confined in the winter as well. In range conditions, keeping such containers by the water holes or bores works extremely well.

There is another option and many Merino farmers have found it works just fine. Instead of mixing the dolomite, sulfur, copper and kelp together, they have six-bin, rain-proof containers. This way the sheep, whatever kind, only take what *they* need. The six bins will hold agricultural salt, ground limestone, dolomite, 99 percent yellow dusting sulfur (in Australia this is usually labeled for orchard use), copper sulfate, and kelp. It interesting to see what the sheep's preferences really are.

One racehorse trainer I know has not just the kelp ad lib, but a container with copper sulfate in each stall, too. She tells me she fills the copper more often than the kelp.

Poison Plants and Fodder Trees

This is a bewildering subject with many animals. Many so-called poisonous plants can be safe at certain times of year, and some apparently all the time. Oleander is one which every authority agrees is lethal, there was even a case of people becoming ill at a barbeque because they impaled the meat on oleander twigs to eat it. Yet I once saw a very healthy looking goat tethered on the median strip of a dual carriage-way, happily eating an oleander. Quite obviously, judging by the state of the plants behind her, she was on her way down the row and had been for a while — the early ones looked decidedly goat-worn. I have seen a horse in the United Kingdom eating yew trees, which can kill in seconds at certain times of the year, without any ill effects at all.

For the purposes of this book, I will list poison plants alphabetically and mark them according to known toxicity or otherwise. This list contains both American and Australian plants and shrubs.

Avocado foliage — palatable, but reduces the milk in lactating animals and causes mastitis if the eating continues.

Azalea — deadly.

Bitter almonds — contain prussic acid.

Blackberries — these only grow on very calcium deficient soils. The thorns would be dangerous in catching up sheep, but the leaves are not poisonous and are very nutritious.

Black nightshade *(Solanum nigrum)* — see deadly nightshade.

Bracken — cumulative poison, but safe if there is plenty of other vegetation. Only grows in humus starved fields. Top-dressing with manure or compost, aerating and generally raising the fertility of the soil with the necessary minerals will totally discourage it. In the Northern Hemisphere small amounts in a paddock are deemed to be beneficial for the sheep to eat it if they need it.

Boobyalla *(Myoporum acuminatum)* — reputedly poisonous, my goats ate it for years. It may be more toxic for sheep.

Capeweed *(Arctotheca calendula)* — a native of South Africa, its toxicity can cause sub-lethal nitrate poisoning; initially it causes magnesium deficiency and then an iodine shortfall. Sheep on it *must* receive dolomite and seaweed (kelp) in some form if they are to survive. Capeweed is a problem which can affect most of the southern part of the continent of Australia (including Tasmania). It can be controlled by aeration, raising the pH of the ground, and balancing the calcium and especially the magnesium in the soil. This enables the grass to compete, which it cannot do if the calcium/magnesium levels are too low. When the capeweed is growing, slashing it several times to stop it coming into seed will also help because the sheep would not find it so palatable, the seed, as with most plants, is reckoned to live in the soil for many years, and when conditions are suitable it germinates and takes over. My last farm had been heavily dolomited (one ton to the acre), the goats had access to seaweed and it was enough to keep them out of trouble, occasionally I had to raise the dolomite a little and give a 10 cc (5 gram) injection of vitamin C to anything scouring persistently, but that was all. According to Dr. Selwyn Everist in his book, *Poison Plants of Australia,* using sprays to control capeweed only makes it more dangerous, especially the use of MCP or 2-4-5T.

Cherry leaves — reputedly poisonous, especially when withered.

Cottonseed — poison constituent gossypol, must be heat treated to be safe; if not treated, it can cause infertility in rams and long-term feeding has been known to cause kidney problems. Nowadays it should also be tested for spray residues and/or GM contamination.

Deadly nightshade *(Solanum nigrum)* — correctly black nightshade; *Solanum americanum* is another variety. Sheep, unless very hungry, avoid both.

Eucalyptus shoots — to be avoided, very high in prussic acid.

Fireweed (*Epilobium angustifolium* or *Madagascariensis*) another African importation. It only grows on very out of balance and poor land. Avoid it, sheep and other animals who graze it die of incurable liver degeneration 18 months after ingestion and it is irreversible. Stock do not usually eat it heavily unless starving. This is a weed which disappears with remineralization and improving the soils; my farmers tell me it is gone within a year.

African grasses — below is a table of the toxicity and other information on African Grasses. This is work done by Dr. Ross Mackenzie of the University of Brisbane and the Queensland DPI.

African-type Grasses				
Grass	Total Oxalate	Ca Total	Intake Ca/Oxalate Balance	Estimated True Ca Digestibility
Non-hazardous				
Flinders	.25	1.92	10.0	99
Rhodes	0.45	1.79	46.1	76
Hazardous				
Pangola	0.92	0.17	- 5.7	39
Green Panic/				
Guinuea Grass	0.81	0.32	- 9.7	42
Para	0.75	0.29	-13.4	24
Kikuyu	1.30	0.23	-22.4	20
Buffel	1.42	0.22	-22.6	16
Narok Setaria	1.81	0.15	-14.2	32
Kazungula Setaria	2.82	0.97	-30.3	3

Ca = Calcium

The hazardous grasses cause Buffel head in horses and full males of apparently all other species. These grasses were only introduced to this country as something was needed to grow on the totally degraded low pH acid soils low in calcium and magnesium.

The fields can be reclaimed by proper remineralization (see next chapter).

Green potatoes — cumulative poison, do not feed.

Heliotrope (Heliotropium amplexicaule) — this is a small plant with multiple pale mauve flowers and silvery leaves. It can be very prevalent in some of the drier districts and is high in copper. Only grows in soils which are very low in the lime minerals (and high in copper). Putting out dolomite ad lib with a little seaweed meal stops the deaths (from the yellows or jaundice) and heliotrope disappears within a year if the land is remineralized. Giving the lick will neutralize the copper and sheep do not die. In one flock of Poll Dorsets, licks consisting of 50 pounds of dolomite and six pounds of kelp meal were enough to stop any deaths when the summer rains brought an out break of heliotrope. Sheep belonging to other farmers, who did not use a lick, did not fare so well. The plant is usually seen after heavy summer rains and grows on ground with a poor lime balance and often a low pH. The high copper is high enough to kill light-colored animals, dark colored ones usually do well on it. As stated, it grows on soils that are generally well supplied with copper but *very* low in the lime minerals.

Laburnum — pods are deadly.

Larkspur — reputedly poisonous.

Laurel — reputedly poisonous.

Lilac — poisons the milk but not the eater.

Linseed — can contain prussic acid, must be boiled for four hours to be safe.

Milkweeds — poison.

Oleander — deadly, in spite of the above anecdote.

Patterson's Curse — same as for heliotrope; however, this is a deep-rooted plant which grows on copper-deficient fields, nature's attempt to bring copper to the surface. Prized by the old European farmers as they knew their stock would not suffer from

Johne's and other diseases due to a lack of copper when it was available in a good mixed pasture.

Peach leaves — poison when withered, best avoided.

Potato haulm — cumulative poison, do not feed.

Privet — as for lilac, poisons the milk, and is not good for young stock to eat either.

Ragwort — only grows on poor calcium/magnesium deficient, compacted soils; remineralizing will stop it.

Rape (canola) — refer to Charles Walters' book *Weeds: Control without Poisons* for a truly grim list of results (page 148).

Red clover — reputedly poisonous, possibly too high in copper for some sheep.

Rhododendron — deadly.

Rhubarb — contains oxalic acid, leaves are poison, affects animals that are not on dolomite more than those that are.

Soursob — same as for rhubarb.

Sorghum — not safe until a yard high, or in seed for preference.

St. John's wort — too high in copper for most white animals, similar to Patterson's Curse in effect and growth habit. Remineralization will discourage it from taking over as it does on poor soils.

Stinkwort — another plant that only grows on soils with very low calcium and magnesium and generally a pH to match, the bottom of the line. I found that the first top-dressing with the required mix (half a ton of dolomite, gypsum and the same of lime) cleared it in a year.

Sudax grass — as for sorghum.

Sugar gums — contain prussic acid, young shoots especially poisonous. Dolomite or powdered chalk is the antidote.

Variegated thistle — same as for capeweed,

Wisteria — doubtful.

Yew trees — poison at certain times of the year (see above) but no one knows which times. I would regard most garden ornamentals and all blue flowered ones with suspicion unless proved otherwise.

Notes and Antidotes

St. John's wort, heliotrope, Patterson's Curse and to a lesser degree red clover seem quite suitable for colored sheep (if they'll eat them), but could be poison for white ones, who do not need so much copper. A teaspoon of dolomite powder and the same of vitamin C powder in a small drench every hour is an antidote to copper poisoning. Vitamin B15 (DADA) by injection will also help, but this is only obtainable from a vet in Australia. In conditions where animals may have to graze these plants, make sure that they receive supplementary dolomite and possibly limestone as well.

Poisons from plants high in prussic acid and/or oxalate are quickly neutralized by drenching pharmaceutical chalk or straight dolomite as soon as possible. A dessertspoon at least for a sheep.

Rhododendron, azalea and possibly oleander poisoning respond very quickly to vitamin C orally, about 10 grams for an adult sheep.

Nitrate poisoning from plants like capeweed can be offset to a certain degree with extra dolomite and seaweed. However, in severe cases (where the blood will show up black on post mortem) vitamin C, according to Dr. Selwyn Everest, is reported to be the only answer. I did not find it worked on goats.

Blood, Henderson and Radostits, in their book *Veterinary Medicine*, are responsible for an extremely comprehensive list of poisons, some quite astonishing ones from the point of view of farmers, white clover is but one. Perhaps it boils down to the fact that any feed in excess and on its own will cause trouble. Legumes, with their ability to deplete iodine, could certainly be regarded as poisonous, but are, in fact, when properly fed, very nourishing. A good guide to poisonous plants in your region will be invaluable.

I have been astonished at the number of poisons vitamin C will detoxify. It was a blind try when it was first used on a friend's goats who were dying from rhododendron poisoning, which they had eaten a week previously and had responded to none of the usual cures. The owner rang me in desperation late at night, all the vitamin C she had in the house were some flavored chewable tablets, so we decided that she should grind up 20 for each goat.

Next morning all were on their feet and grazing bar one, and even she responded after a second dose of vitamin C.

Many of these "weeds" are not native to the countries where they have taken over — this particularly applies to Australia, but, as Charles Walters and others have pointed out, if land is abused enough the good fodder species will not grow, but something will — usually something like fireweed (mentioned above) or worse.

Note: In days gone by pastoralists in Europe expected their pastures to contain at least 65 varieties of plants, including several that we would designate as noxious or poisonous. These plants all have a medicinal value and stock could thus monitor their own health. Newman Turner (a doctor and the author of *Fertility Farming* mentioned in the bibliography), was able with pastures of this kind to buy animals afflicted with Johne's disease or tuberculosis and make full use of their genetic potential without causing any harm to his own stock, and the purchases (mainly cattle) did indeed recover their own health in most cases.

Fodder Trees

This should really be part of the overall farm strategy. Using fodder trees in shelter belts is an excellent standby. There are quite a few native Australian trees, some slow growing, others that grow as fast as the many non-indigenous species now available. Many of these already grow in the United States. Most European trees will grow in practically any part of Australia with a little care, water and attention, naturally they grow faster in areas of higher rainfall.

It is just as important to remineralize for trees. The correct calcium and magnesium levels are as necessary for them as they are for pasture species. One of my clients, who had just had a soil analysis done showing excessively low lime mineral levels, complained that 100 trees he had planted four years ago had not grown at all — they could not. Now that he is remineralizing the farm, they should grow well.

All trees like soils that are reasonably well drained and balanced. If you want trees to grow well, have the soil analyzed and the lime minerals brought right up to their correct levels. Trees on sour soils with a low pH often begin to show signs of die-back after a few years. Superphosphate also causes this effect. I bought a well-treed farm, which showed on closer examination that all the trees had bad die-back. Superphosphate and muriate of potash had been used annually and the soil audit was a disaster. The first application of the necessary lime minerals brought the trees back to life and helped to improve the very sour pastures as well.

A shelter belt should consist of slow growing trees with faster growing ones on the outside. Fences will be needed when the trees are young, but as they mature, sheep could safely be allowed to have access to them. They will only start to ring-bark and damage the trees if their copper reserves are too low. Their dung round the trees where they camp can only be beneficial.

Slower growing trees include:

European Oak — all varieties.
European Ash — all varieties.
Apple, pear and nut — all edible.
Kurrajong — a great drought standby that regrows after trimming.
All pine trees — the needles dead or alive are palatable and high in minerals.

Medium growing trees include:

All the casuarinas — including she-oak, bull-oak; these trees stand trimming almost indefinitely, these are also nitrogen fixers.
All eucalypts.
All wattles — these have a limited life in dryer districts, are nitrogen fixing, and in virgin rainforests they grow to great girth and height.
Elm trees — they sucker freely and the suckers make good fodder.
Poplar trees — all kinds, they also sucker freely and roots run up to 40 meters (sideways).

Faster growing trees include:

Tagasaste (Tree Lucern) — *only* in well-drained, dry situations. These can have a goitrogenic affect if fed exclusively, seaweed would have to be supplied to stop the effect. They are also totally allergic to Glyphosate in any form, whatever the name, and will die within a few days even when well grown if the sprays are used near them. They can, in fact, be used as an indicator of the presence of the chemical.

Coprosma (mirror bush).

Willow — any variety, as long as the area is fairly wet, very invasive roots, except for Chilean willow, which grows fast from slips and, if layered will make a solid shelter wall, does not like high temperatures or hard frosts.

Paulownas — likes conditions similar to tagasaste but better rainfall, dislikes excessive dry or frosts when young.

Trees like tagasaste and some of the willows will benefit from fairly hard trimming, and the farmer will have to do some of the harvesting. Many of these trees also produce a cash return if properly grown. Neal Kinsey, in his talks, emphasizes that trees, whatever kind, *also* need a balanced soil.

Chapter 6

Land Management

This is the single most important item in any farming enter-prise, be it fine-wool sheep breeding, meat sheep, dairying or stud breeding. Land management is the difference between ultimate success or failure. All disciplines demand land in very good heart mineral-wise. Without all the minerals being available in the right quantities, the microbes, mycorrhizae and other occupants of the soil cannot do their work to make it a living, breathing food facto-ry which will nurture all who live off it.

A soil analysis is mandatory, and in the words of a certain Professor who spoke at a Beef Forum in South Australia in 1991, "An analysis should always be performed by a firm that does *not* sell anything except analyses." An analysis from such a firm is shown below; it compares favorably with the two best known firms in the United States where soil audits (as they are often called) are taken extremely seriously.

A year or two back I was lead-in speaker for Neal Kinsey (a back-up for curly questions about stock of all kinds). Neal expounded at length on what I have just said. Neal had the good fortune at one stage in his career to work with Dr. William A. Albrecht. Again and again people in the audience would ask his opinion of this or that soil conditioner, etc. The seminar Neal gave ran five days in all and the participants were still asking questions

Example of a Soil Analysis from a Tennessee Farm

Item	Result	Desirable Level
Color: grey brown		
Texture: clay loam		
pH (1:5 Water)	5.9	5.5 - 7.5
pH (1:5 0.01 c12)	5.3	
Electrical Conductivity, EC us/cm	91	<300
Total Soluble Salt, TSS ppm	300.3	<990
Available calcium, Ca ppm	780	1650
Available magnesium, Mg ppm	133.2	175
Available sodium, Na ppm	39.1	<139
Available hydrogen, H ppm	66	<24
Available nitrogen, N ppm	9.30	20
Available phosphorus, P ppm	14.10	20
Available potassium, K ppm	136.50	110
Available sulfur, S ppm	3	5
Available copper, Cu ppm	1.2	2
Available zinc, Zn ppm	3	5
Available iron, Fe ppm	27	>20
Available manganese, Mn ppm	89	>20
Available cobalt, Co ppm	5	.5-.7
Available molybdenum, Mo ppm	.4	.5-.7
Available boron, B ppm	.2	.4-.6
Total Organic Matter, OM %	3.80	3-4
Total phosphorus, TPN ppm	1124	
Cation Exchange Capacity, CEC	11.13	
Exchange Sodium Percentage, ESP	1.43	<5
Calcium/Magnesium Ratio, Ca/Mg	3.51	2-4

Percentages of Ca, Mg, Na, K and percentage of CEC

	Percentage	Percentage of CEC
Exchangeable calcium, Ca	38.8%	56.76%
Exchangeable magnesium, Mg	11.1%	17.55%
Exchangeable sodium, Na	01.1%	4.94%
Exchangeable potassium, K	03.15%	3.59%
Exchangeable hydrogen, H	50.9	17.11%

Recommendations:

Gypsum	0 tons to acres
Lime	0.51 tons to acre
Dolomite	0.20 tons to acre

Example of a Soil Analysis from a Tennessee Farm (cont.)

Recommendations:
    In addition:
        Copper: .25 kg to the acre
        Zinc: 0
        Cobalt: 0
        Molybdenum: 0
        Iron: 0
        Manganese: 0
        Boron: .10 kg to the acre

Notes:

1) The 5.3 calcium pH means that trace minerals must not be spread on this farm, but since we know the shortcomings, they can be added to the feed or lick.

2) On a farm where the CEC is much higher, sometimes the recommendation for lime can be in excess of a ton to the acre (two tons to the hectare). In that case, the lime mineral application should be halved and the second half be applied not sooner than eight or nine months after the first application.

3) I have seen recommendations here (often emanating from the United States) where four or five tons to the hectare is suggested. I had to undo this on a farm where it had been spread. The animals were dying of an induced magnesium deficiency, and some were too far gone to save.

at the end. Neal reiterated endlessly that the single most important input was the soil analysis and balancing the main lime minerals, but they still kept asking.

The analysis above is taken from a farm in Tennessee, which is similar to many of those found in Australia. The calcium and magnesium were way out of balance with a pH to match. In this case, it means that some of the trace minerals will not be available to the sheep until the main minerals are back on track. The pastures will not have very good quality grasses until the calcium (under half the desired level) and magnesium (roughly two thirds of the desired level) ratios are corrected. The ground cover may be poor quality.

Dr. Newman Turner was a farmer in the United Kingdom just after World War II who was faced with a farm totally ruined by the wartime protocols of forcing high production with NPK fertilizers. This practice resulted in a very high rate of Johne's disease in the stock and Crohn's in Dr. Turner. He worked on those pastures until he had 65 varieties of mixed grasses, clovers and so-called weeds. He was then able to buy in diseased stock and watch them recover as they selected the plants *they* needed from the pasture. *Fertility Pastures*, which can be found in the Acres U.S.A. book catalog, was the result.

There are however quite as many problems on country with a high pH, which is more usual in the United States. (while in Australia I have been confronted with pHs as low as 3.5). The reason is still the same, but imbalances of the main minerals on high pH areas are not as easy to rectify as those on more acid country. However, on the land with a pH above 5.8 (calcium) missing trace minerals may be spread without the risk of losing them all as happens if they are spread on soils with a low pH. Regrettably the people who sell the trace minerals for this purpose do not point this out.

Regardless of the pH, the most important factor is to bring the calcium and magnesium into their correct balance, which is ideally around 80 percent calcium to 20 percent magnesium, the exact ratios differing according to the Cation Exchange Capacity. High sodium is often a component of these soils, throwing everything else out of balance. The sulfur on this audit is reasonable; if it was not, gypsum (calcium sulfate) could be used to bring it into balance. This material is also useful in quite small amounts, a quarter of a ton to the acre, to bring salt affected soils back into balance. This work was pioneered in the United States.

Hydrogen

This shows me (who rarely sees a farm) just how sick the pasture is. Without proper hydrogen levels the CEC cannot be worked out. As the acidity proceeds, the hydrogen ions push out the necessary calcium, magnesium, potash, and phosphorus on the colloid soil particles. When the hydrogen shows a high level, the soil is very sick.

Cation Exchange Capacity.

This always causes some difficulty to the untrained and it did to me for ages. I read a very good description in an excellent article on soils in the March 1999 *Acres U.S.A.*: "In simple terms, the ability of the soil to hold on and then to release cations from the clay particles is called the soil's Cation Exchange Capacity, or its CEC." The soil pH, hydrogen and mineral levels affect the CEC,

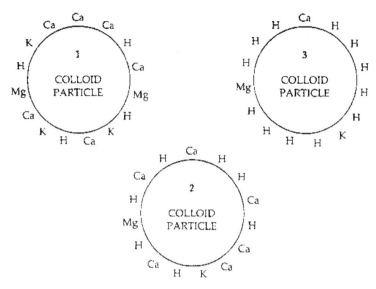

1. *Shows a healthy soil particle with adequate minerals. Calcium (C), Magnesium (Mg), Potassium (K) and Hydrogen (H) ranged around it. The pH of this land would be about 6.0+.*
2. *Shows the soil starting to degenerate, the hydrogen ions are beginning to displace the calcium, magnesium and potassium. The pH would be falling quite fast and be about 5.0 or lower.*
3. *Shows the final stage when there is only 1 ion of calcium, magnesium and potassium left — not enough to maintain healthy life. The hydrogen has taken over, and until it can be replaced in its turn by the calcium and the other two minerals, the soil will be unable to grow healthy feed — weeds will proliferate.*

which roughly indicates the "strength" of the land. CEC at the 1.5 level, which can occur on very poor country (in Australia), shows a soil much in need of help. This can only be rectified quite slowly, as the soil could not hold a higher application of any material at one time. Where the organic matter is low, it can be raised by mulching and the soil improvement will be hastened. On one very poor farm (mine) we started with a CEC of 9, five years later it is up to 23.

Spreading the Lime Minerals

On this analysis the calcium and magnesium are too low; the calcium particularly is half what it should be. The magnesium is about two thirds of the requirement. Sulfur levels are good and this will help with the production of good wool.

The application of the amounts suggested will start the farm on the road to recovery. In a case of this sort it is wise to re-analyze about one year later. In any farm activity where the animals are run at a high stocking rate, it is wise to run the analysis about very three years.

Safe Amounts of Lime

These have been covered in notes two and three above, which is why I suggest that farmers ring me before they apply the necessary minerals. Where the amounts suggested come well above this figure we usually divide the applications into two or even three, leaving at least 6 months between applications. When the gypsum and dolomite are added, the amount spread can come over this figure; it is safe to spread them all in one application. It is the high amount of lime that can throw the soil badly out of balance by creating an artificial magnesium deficiency. This is *extremely* dangerous if stock are involved. If cropping, these figures are not so important because the lime will be well absorbed before stock graze the land again.

Some years ago I was called to a farm in dire straights. There were 4,000 acres of crops, Merino sheep and red poll cattle. The cattle had gone mad and the rest of the farm was littered with very well grown dead Merino weaners. It was a well-run conventional farm, superphosphate and lime being spread over the whole area annually (most farmers do not spread the lime at the same time, although this was recommended many years ago). Lime and super had knocked the magnesium (if any) right out of the food chain.

Superphosphate, as we now know, locks up 10 pounds of magnesium to the acre (according to André Voisin, it also inhibits copper 100 percent). Spreading lime without magnesium has the same effect, as too much lime inhibits magnesium (too high magnesium can have the same effect on calcium). This farm had literally run out of magnesium in a space of a week after many years of the program. The 500 cattle which had been running their huge paddock non-stop for days were halted immediately by putting out eight 44-gallon drums (split longways) of dolomite. Once the cattle found the mineral they stayed eating it until it was all gone and then turned away to graze normally as though nothing had happened. Stopping the deaths of the weaners took a little longer and fifteen tons of very expensive, high-magnesium dolomite (magnesite, sometimes called keiserite) had to be spread by air and then the sheep stopped dying. After that episode the cattle and sheep were put onto the stock lick referred to in this book, the land was analyzed and top-dressed and it all settled down satisfactorily.

Balancing the Lime Minerals

The object of the exercise is to bring the calcium and magnesium levels into balance and thereby raise the pH to a desirable level, around 6.5 (calcium). This is within .5 of neutral (7.0), above which the soil becomes alkaline, which is equally undesirable.

The bones and general health of the stock on this farm above cannot be as good as they should be without the correct calcium and magnesium in the soil. The lick already mentioned, which should be out 365 days a year, is a standby for drought and different climatic conditions. In the blood picture of a healthy sheep, the calcium at 2.3 ug/ml per liter should be approximately twice the amount of the magnesium at 1.0 ug/ml per liter. The phosphorus should be around the same level as the magnesium and not above it as is so often advised.

Phosphorus

There is no concern about the phosphorus, this is a grazing farm and with a bank of 1,124 ppm of locked-up phosphorus, which will start to feed back into the system once the lime minerals are brought up to their correct level. There are now quite an appreciable number of farmers in Australia who have seen or heard Neal Kinsey, either on video, audio tape or in person. As mentioned, he once worked with Dr. William A. Albrecht and continued carrying on after Dr. Albrecht's death. Kinsey explains time and time again that phosphorus can *not* be utilized unless there is adequate calcium (and magnesium).

The locked-up phosphorus level has become a familiar sight since it was first included in an analysis a few years ago. In fact, I have yet to see an analysis where there is none. There comes a stage with phosphatic and nitrogenous fertilizers when the trace minerals are totally inhibited, particularly copper, a trace mineral without which it is impossible to have healthy and productive sheep or plants. Putting out copper with phosphorus, as was often done in the past, does not work either. Superphosphate ties up copper 100 percent. As the pH rises, the locked-up minerals will become obtainable to the stock and plants. On my present small block (the CEC improvement is mentioned above, from 9 to 23) the copper started at .2 ppm and after five years and three top-dressings it is eight ppm. It is higher than the recommended level and the goats, horses and one 18-year-old black Merino still come into the yard to drink water from an old washing copper.

It was my good fortune to grow up before the age of super-phosphate and general NPK farming. Animal manure provided the P (phosphorus) and N (nitrogen) in the soil as the barns and yards were cleared after each winter. I do appreciate that farmers brought up in the NPK era have difficulty with this. One of my New Zealand farmers has 4,000 acres and the same number of Merinos. He crops to augment the sheep's diets in winter, etc., and all that leaves the farm are fat lambs and wool. After we had analyzed with a result rather like the one in this chapter, I said I knew he would want to put some "super" on the crop paddock, but suggested he only do half of it. However, he said he would take my word for it and nothing bar the lime minerals would be applied. In Australia and New Zealand new drills were invented to carry the seed and pelleted super, so he had to find an old combine (as I had to do earlier) so all his contemporaries knew what he was up to. He endured five months of extreme sarcasm and rude remarks, which, however, quieted as the crop grew. Finally it was harvested and it was the best seen in that part of New Zealand for 25 years.

Aerating

An aerator, properly used when the ground has had about 100 ml of rain, is equal to a quarter of a ton of neutralizing material per year. On four different farms, which started with a lower pH than the above, the goal of pH 6.5 and a healthy calcium/magnesium ratio has been reached in four and a half years. At that stage, if the farm is properly looked after, the system comes somewhere near being sustainable. However, it *must* be realized that unbalanced calcium and magnesium are the main cause of rock hard ground, these levels *must* be adjusted before aerating.

Sodium

Not all farms have sodium as low as this one. Only too often iron and salt are dangerously high, leaving all else in short supply. In the late 1980s, we bought a farm where the salt was 600 times too high and the iron 1,600 times too high (pH 4.3). This meant in effect that every other mineral was virtually unobtainable. One ton of dolomite to the acre resolved the situation in 18 months. Those unbalanced figures were the result of superphosphate and muriate of potash being used annually for many years. Artificial potash, whether muriate or chloride, raises the salt table (see below).

Potash (Potassium)

Both muriate of potash and sulphate of potash top-dressings are extremely sodic. Muriate raises the salt well over 100 percent and sulphate raises it 43.2 percent (according to Dr. Harold Willis, writing in *Acres U.S.A.*). Once the soil comes back into balance potash is self-renewing. This was discovered in the Haughley Experiment which ran for 15 years in the United Kingdom after World War II. Potash loss was shown to be a permanent and ongoing problem on the conventionally and chemically farmed half of the experiment in spite of potash applications. On the old-fashioned naturally farmed half of the farm, the potassium was more than adequately replaced naturally each year.

The farm in the analysis is also fortunate to have potassium almost at a good, right level for the reasons mentioned above. When the system is organic or becoming so, it fairly soon gets back into its rhythm of potash being freely available at all times. Replacing potash artificially is difficult.

Potassium deficiencies in sheep can be alleviated by adding cider vinegar to fodder, hay or water to offset the risk of dystokia (pulling lambs), probably the most damaging of the deficiencies of that mineral. On the over-farmed, parched land of Southern Victoria (Australia) where we first settled and a great deal of my time, unpaid, was spent extracting lambs for the neighboring farmers, I felt sorry for the ewes. Some of those lambs felt as though they were set in concrete.

Sulfur

The good sulfur levels on the farm above will help the sheep in making full use of any feed they can get. The amino acids of sulfur, particularly methionine and cysteine assist the gut to assimilate selenium. A lack of sulfur also means the sheep will get lice and other exterior parasites. Had the sulfur been low, the application of gypsum (calcium sulfate) would have helped this mineral to recover. Sulfur is another mineral that becomes locked up by artificials where superphosphate has been regularly used. Originally I did not expect land that had been top-dressed with super would suffer this way because of the sulfuric acid that is used in its manufacture. Neal Kinsey told me in November 1998 that sulfur deficiencies worldwide were growing at an alarming rate.

Zinc

This is at a good level. The two animals that seem to require high amounts of zinc are pigs and alpacas. Sheep will show facial eczema in rare cases if zinc is very low, but the addition of seaweed in the licks (it is well supplied with zinc) is usually enough to stop a shortfall. This trace mineral is now reported to be inhibited like the others with the extended use of artificials. A lack of zinc in the food chain is the major cause of foot and mouth outbreaks.

Iron

It is rare to have to supply iron to stock and feeding it is not desirable, as iron suppresses vitamin E in the system. The amount shown on the analysis above will be enough. Anemia can be caused by a deficiency of iron, but in nearly all cases the reason is usually a lack of copper, as without that mineral the iron cannot be utilized. In cases where iron is too low, fish products can be added to the diet. Meat derivatives such as blood and bone are not and never have been safe, unless the source is very carefully monitored. In most countries they have in any case been banned for herbivores since May 1996 due to BSE (Bovine Spongiform Encephalitis or Mad Cow disease). However further research by Mark Purdey has proved fairly conclusively that meat meal is *not* the cause of BSE (see the chapter on ailments).

Boron

Boron is another mineral that has become a casualty of chemical farming. When it is too low, sheep suffer arthritis and bone problems. Nut trees, legumes, certain root vegetables and some grain crops cannot grow properly unless there is adequate boron in the soil, another reason for having a regular soil audit done. In an article on "Medicinal Properties of Whole Foods" *(Townsend Letter for Doctors*, May 2003) it stated that the proper absorption of magnesium depended on adequate boron.

Organic Matter

This is at the base of the page and is an all-important fraction of this or any other soil analysis. Its importance is demonstrated by the following anecdote. Two farms with exactly similar (and disastrous) soil pictures in two different states in Australia, one with organic matter in the region of 11, and the other with organic matter at a level of 1.1. The first farm had no apparent stock problems; they would arise in a matter of a year or two, but as the owner took the necessary measures to rectify the lime deficiencies, the stock are and will remain in excellent health. On the second farm the stock were already dying, organic matter holds the nutrients and gives the pasture something to grow on. Nowadays stubble retention, direct drilling (without sprays) and good farming practices like slashing and aerating are helping to preserve and ultimately raise the organic matter.

The low pH is to a point a result of the good organic matter, which is of course acid. It also means that until the pH can be raised by the top-dressing of lime minerals (after analysis) and the ensuing aeration, none of the trace minerals will be available to the stock. I have recounted in other books how on a farm much worse than this the trace minerals started to come back into the feed chain in about 18 months, particularly the cobalt, which is a dangerous and difficult mineral to feed. Sheep farmers usually replace this with vitamin B12 injections, and occasionally actual cobalt sulfate additions to the licks or water (see previous chapters). Hopefully raising the health of the soil will make these strategies unnecessary.

Burning Off

Burning off crop residue is a potent cause of low organic matter, not only does the organic matter disappear but, according to Bill Mollison (of Permaculture fame), significantly large amounts of many important minerals disappear with it.

Nitrogen, 54-75 percent, will be replaced in 11 years by legumes and rain.

Phosphorous, 27-50 percent, will be replaced in 20 years by rain.

Potassium, 43-66 percent.

Calcium, 31-34 percent.

Magnesium, 25-43 percent.

Boron, 35-54 percent.

These levels were worked out from bush fires. Even if burning off paddock wastes produces only half these losses, it is still very serious.

Organic Inputs from Off-farm

Inputs of organic material to augment the manure from the stock, and a small amount of lime, dolomite or gypsum when a new analysis indicates it, should be all that is needed. It is only when a farm is selling off large amounts of grain or hay that fairly steady remineralization is needed, as well as a method of replacing the lost organic matter. Large scale composting using municipal wastes as well as on farm crop wastes is something that many farmers will have to consider one day — it is already beginning to happen. In the United States, Fletcher Sims and Malcolm Beck have both made art forms of composting nearly all wastes.

Fungal Conditions

The great curse of degraded land with unbalanced pH is the proliferation of fungal conditions, ranging from the various staggers to 250 listed fungal diseases (Dr. Alenstein, DVM, in *Hoard's Dairyman*). Many of these are very difficult to impossible to cure, even if not immediately fatal. Most of them cause long lasting and apparently irreversible hormone damage in both sexes.

Dr. William Albrecht explained this very neatly. When the soil is sour enough, the soil fungi (mycorrhizae) become infected and act as harmful fungi. They proliferate and infect the plant roots, which in turn infect the plant that is trying to grow and this infects the sheep, lambs, etc. Spraying to kill the fungus is obviously not an option. Remineralizing and restoring the soil health is the only answer to this problem. Drugs for animals and the soil do *not* fill the bill. Neal Kinsey makes it quite clear that rust and fungal-type disease only arise when the copper has been lost, usually due to overuse of NPK fertilizers.

There is no shortcut to remineralizing and raising soil fertility. If it is not ultimately done, the sheep and their products will not prosper. Licks are really an adjunct to good farming, generally used to tide the animals over the lean patches that occur in prolonged dry spells or when the feed first comes away after autumn and winter. They will hold the sheep until such time as the farm starts to recover, and are a Band-Aid resource at that stage.

Chapter 7

Management of Sheep

Handling

From time immemorial, first humans, then dogs and horses have controlled sheep. Some graziers still use these old methods, which manage the sheep far more quietly than the two, three or four-wheeled vehicles generally used nowadays. In my youth the emphasis in any kind of livestock handling was to keep the beasts as calm as possible.

It is important that a steady form of management is used so that the sheep become accustomed to being fed, moved, yarded or whatever in as stress-free a manner as possible. Few people moving sheep or anything at full speed seem to realize that frantic chasing can affect an animal's health just as surely as starvation. This is especially true if the sheep are low on magnesium for any reason (generally because it is low in the farm soil, or the farm has been top-dressed with super). Stressful handling can, in those circumstances, cause death by tetany, which means a lack of magnesium in most cases.

When taking delivery of a new flock of sheep, try to find out the methods used on the previous farm. New mobs of sheep that have been used to different methods of handling from those in use on your farm may experience difficulties when they first arrive.

Patience will be necessary until they get used to the new management.

My favorite story was told to me by an old sheep farmer; he was having a terrible job persuading a new flock to go through a gateway. Finally he went up to the house and called his wife out to help. She came straight out with her apron on. The moment she appeared one of the rams detached itself from the rest and ran up to her bleating. She walked through the gate and the whole mob followed her and the ram and all was well. Apparently he had been bottle reared by a lady who wore an apron.

It is especially important to train young lambs and weaners to be hand fed, farms where this has not been done find it very difficult to persuade their sheep into taking licks or anything else out of a trough for that matter. These are an ongoing part of good animal husbandry. It may not always be necessary to hand feed, but licks should be available at all times and if it takes a month to teach the sheep what the licks are for, it may be too late and they could succumb to a deficiency condition.

Identification

I first met the colored tag system when working in Western Australia in 1993. I would ask the age of a mob and be told that they were Red Tags, which to me with a crossbred sheep background meant absolutely nothing. Eventually I realized that each color meant a year, a very clear system of identification when running large numbers of Merinos. It is an eight year rotation and my experience begins with:

1987, 1995, Light green ear tags
1988, 1996, Purple ear tags
1989, 1997, Yellow ear tags
1990, 1998, Red ear tags
1991, 1999, Blue ear tags
1992, 2000, Black ear tags
1993, 2001, White ear tags
1994, 2002, Orange ear tags
2003 starts on light green again and so on

Obviously sheep in the United States will have a different color code and some of flocks of sheep in eastern Australia use the system, but not all. It seems to me an eminently sensible method.

Handling Routines

When feeding sheep in periods when feed is short, one should endeavor to follow a set routine so that the animals soon learn they do not have to circle the hopper or the pick-up truck towing it at full speed in order to get fed. Similarly, when yarding a quiet, set routine should be followed. There used to be farmer in our district years ago who conducted what was known as the sheep derby. He always moved his animals from place to place at a good gallop, and his sheep had a worried look about them.

It is an education to watch a good drover moving his stock along on the roadsides. They maintain their three or four miles a day without apparent effort. Drovers generally use dogs and/or horses in addition to their vehicles. Sheep moved thus have to fatten on the road and reach their destination in the same kind of order that they would have been in had they come from a good pasture. Hence the old term "the long paddock" when farmers take to the roads with their sheep in times of drought and stress. This I thought to be an occupation only found in Australia until I read about some of the big cattle treks in the United States in the old days.

Permanent Yards and Their Disadvantages

As in all livestock operations it pays to have the best yards and handling complexes possible. Each flock master will have rather set ideas on this — the result of many years experience. However, there are new technologies available and some are worth consideration.

Portable yards definitely have their place, and, as time goes on they have improved both in design and ease of erection. They are an important weapon against soil-borne infections like CLA (caseous lymphadenitis) and polyarthritis. It was found in South Africa that the former disease was greatly reduced when handling yards were moved to fresh ground each year. This strategy was more effective than the vaccinations offered. Vaccinations do *not* take the place of good management.

Nor should mulesing, tail-docking or marking (castrating) take place in the same area twice. If it is done two times in the same year or two years running, it is better husbandry to move the yards to a new piece of ground each time. The causative agent for polyarthritis, navel ill or whatever it is called, is corynebacteria, quite the most difficult to control and/or cure. This has already been covered and the best strategy is to place the lamb down on its legs — a matter of handling animals a few seconds longer in order to avoid exposing fresh wounds to the ground. Exposing raw flesh to soil is *not* desirable. The bacterium (with others) lives in the ground where sheep have gathered in any numbers such as yards or camps and enters the body via a cut or navel cord (blackleg or tetanus can start the same way). Liming the yards heavily after each use would go some way to controlling these sort of outbreaks, as nearly all germs thrive in acid conditions, but it will not be the complete answer. Humane treatment of animals goes a long way toward avoiding infectious conditions.

Covered Yards

The once yearly possibility of rain when the sheep are in for shearing is expensive in the times when it happens. I have seen at least one farm where the shearing shed had enough shedding to hold big numbers in the dry, so that rain did not affect operations. This particular farm had large roofed areas which could and did double for sale or display yards. They can also be a commercial option to lease out when not required by the owner. The time lost in waiting for sheep to dry, getting shearers back to do them when they are, which often means the next farmer has to wait his turn is something to avoid if at all possible.

Lambing Times

Spring or autumn lambing has already been discussed. One of the biggest arguments against spring lambing, which certainly has its advantages, is tender wool, because the break might occur in the middle and not at the end of the staple due to changing dates around. That does not really hold water because tender wool is a nutritional problem and if licks are available all the year and hand feeding done when necessary it should become a thing of the past. Also, as the land is improved by the measures suggested in the last chapter, that particular stress will be minimized and possibly eliminated all together.

Occasionally farmers say to me that they never hand feed animals. It seems to me, especially on farms that grow their own feed, that one cannot lay down a rule like that. Australia is notorious for rogue weather patterns and they do not just occur here, the United States would at times be just as prone to bad weather. I feel the condition of the flocks should be the yardstick. Once a beast goes down in health and loses condition it is very expensive to get it back to square one again, but preventing it with a bit of judicious feed when the occasion demands makes a lot of sense. Given the vicissitudes in the sheep industry, presenting animals for sale in top order seems to be the way to go. In bad years the poorly conditioned sheep just do not make it worth trucking them to market in some cases. It is, however, noticeable that even in those bad years the offerings which are in good store condition usually make their price.

Cull Ewes and Their Lambs

Sorting out the cull ewes and getting the maximum out of them before they are sold is a perennial problem on most studs. One farm I saw in Western Australia in 1993 had an unusual answer, which was to have Suffolk rams to put over these ewes. The resulting lambs and their mothers were easy to see, as they stayed together, and both could be drafted off when necessary. Due to hybrid vigor, the lambs matured early and fetched (at the time I saw that particular farm) some of the best prices since the bad downturn in Australia at the end of the eighties. Some farmers tell me they cannot do this because of black hairs in the clip, but the majority agree that it does not happen and the method is sound.

Dipping, Jetting, Etc.

Other familiar sheep operations are dipping, jetting or whatever strategies are used for controlling fly or lice outbreaks. These outbreaks should not occur when the feed is correct and all the minerals are in balance — again the licks and land improvement are the key. In time these tasks should become redundant. Making sure the correct amount of sulfur, copper and the other contents of

Sheep in covered yard.

Covered yard complex.

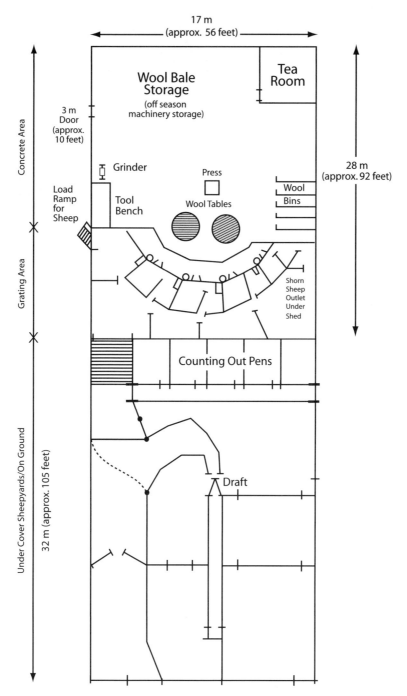

Plan of a covered yard complex.

The shearing board.

the lick are available to the sheep at *all* times ensures that those operations will become a thing of the past.

Organic Wool

The call for organic, uncontaminated wool will increase. Organic cotton is already in demand, and if natural fibers are to compete with the synthetics in the marketplace, organic wool should become a fact of life. It is not so difficult to arrange, and doing it will save the farmer money and handling. The emphasis will not be on strategic drenching, dipping, etc., but on shearing and breeding, which will become the major jobs in a sheep enterprise, hopefully making the sheep farmer's life a little easier. In Australia the demand for organic wool first came from Germany in the late 1990s. The Germans wanted it for the cosmetics and medical industries which of course needed it for the lanolin.

Lambing Troubles

Lambing traumas can be improved as far as pulling lambs is concerned, avoiding it is a matter of diet. Dystokia is a condition due to a lack of potassium in the diet. Feeding cider vinegar to the dams as suggested, either by watering it onto hay or mixing in the feed at least once a week for several weeks coming up to lambing, should be enough to virtually make pulling lambs manually a thing of the past. This applies to all breeds.

Fostering Lambs

I had forgotten how this was done in the United Kingdom until I came across a book about the Land Army during and after World War II. Land girls got on well with sheep and there was a description on how to foster lambs onto other ewes whose own young had died. My granddaughter described to me the same process, which her father used (he is shearer). He skinned the dead lamb, made four holes for the new lamb's legs to go through and the deprived ewe took to the lamb at once. There was an almost instant bonding; obviously ewe's milk is preferable to a replacer and it is less trouble to have the lamb out in the field with the rest of the flock than trying to hand-rear it.

Predators

The problem of how to deal with predators remains. Feral dogs, crows, foxes, coyotes and packs of domestic unrestrained dogs — all of these can all cause terrible damage. Within reason I guess that the healthier and the more active the ewes, the less chance there is of successful attacks. Using horses to work with crossbreeds in the '60s and '70s, I used to ride around with a long tar-stick once or even twice a day when lambing was at its peak. Each newly born lamb would be given a dab of Stockholm Tar (which has a distinctive smell) on its back, this was enough to mask the odor of the lamb from the fox (but apparently not from the ewe) until the lamb was strong enough to keep out of trouble. It was not necessary to get off the mare for this operation, she was extremely interested in lambs. When I lived in the mountains some years ago, it was an area of very poor soil and rabbits were not much in evidence; this had driven the foxes and wild dogs to changing their diet to new-born lambs. The farmers took shifts at night during lambing, armed with spotlights and guns, as the foxes used to sit behind the ewes as they lambed and took the lambs as they were born. A few rabbits are probably preferable.

Packs of marauding dogs are another problem, several good marksmen in the right place at the right time are the only answer there. Farmers in some districts have gotten together to beat this menace when it occurs, which is too often when the farms are near big towns. A friend of mine used to be able to pick the marauders off in a mob with his rifle while driving his tractor — he was a very good marksman.

There is another option these days and that is guard animals: dogs, llamas, alpacas and even donkeys are being used effectively. All have been successful for many years now. I believe with dogs that bonding the dog to a particular mob can take a bit of time, and has to be repeated if the mob is sold. This does not happen with llamas, alpacas or donkeys, and even better they eat the same fodder as the sheep. The camelids (alpacas & llamas) rarely suffer predator damage — especially when the males are kept in the same paddocks as the breeders and sheep. A friend told me that the sight of a male alpaca at full speed with its head stuck straight out going after a very large fox was a sight not to be forgotten.

Teeth

Good feeding of the bone-building minerals will go a long way towards avoiding bad mouth problems. Teeth do not become loose and stick in odd directions in sheep that are properly supplied with minerals all their lives. The teeth may wear down, but will do so evenly and the sheep are able to forage quite effectively even when the teeth are level with the jaw. As long as the tooth wear is even, the animals are not disadvantaged at all.

Feet

Much the same applies to feet. Proper minerals will save many hours of handling, and the old timer's method of taking a mob out on the roads at regular intervals for four or five hours and keeping them moving was a very good foot trimmer. Obviously anything that is lame must be trimmed up, but usually a lack of any of the minerals in the lick, particularly copper is the cause of trouble. Wet years do *not* cause a predisposition to foot problems in sheep (or anything else) but a lack of adequate copper certainly does.

Copper and Early Lambing

For many years I wondered why sheep did not become sexually active at the same age as goats. In the latter the does are fit to be mated by the time they are five to seven months or even younger. Goats are an animal that do not do well without the right amount of copper. One sheep grazier I know found that when he first put out the licks already mentioned in this book, it was necessary for him to separate the ewe and ram lambs by the time they were four months (as would happen in any goat herd). When first he had the licks out the ewe lambs all dropped *their* lambs at a year old much to the horror of his vet. But the farmer pointed out that the ewes looked exceptionally well on it and he was not worried. The vet was. At one point he decided to take a worm count to see what was happening, the count was between 100 and 200 and when he asked the farmer what he was going to do about that the answer was: "Well if they look as well as that with those few worms they can keep them and I will not bother to drench them!" He did not and as they were on the lick with adequate copper, the worms did not become a problem anyway. Worms are another sign of inadequate copper in the diet according to Dr. William A. Albrecht.

Chapter 8

Minerals

If the minerals are in total balance, vitamin deficiencies should not occur. In other words, behind every vitamin shortfall there is a lack of minerals. The saying: "If a little is good, more must be better" does *not* apply to minerals. Whether it is on the soil or in the body of the sheep, the amounts that can be used are fairly exact.

The lick for Merino sheep is made up as follows:

25 kg (55 pounds) dolomite (calcium magnesium carbonate, a.k.a. dolomitic limestone)
4 kg (9 pounds) yellow dusting sulphur
4 kg (9 pounds) copper sulfate
4 kg (9 pounds) urea-free seaweed meal

For crossbreeds reduce the copper sulfate to two kg if desired; although farmers who have crossbreeds tell me that they too manage fine on the standard lick, they just do not take so much. As stated in earlier chapters, this lick has to be kept *dry,* and grain sprinkled on the top may be used as a starter. For those on cobalt deficient soils consult the section on that mineral for the amount to add to the lick.

The other option for supplying minerals is to provide a six-bin arrangement and put all the above in four bins of the container, with salt and ground limestone in the other two. This must, of course, be weatherproof but many sheep farmers have found it very successful.

Always use as basic a form of minerals as possible. It appears that the simpler the form of minerals in the diet, the better they are assimilated. Nowadays we have the advantage of good seaweed products, so we do not have to go around with the Lugol's Solution of Iodine permanently on hand for deficiencies. Like most natural substances, kelp provides far safer and more effective iodine supplementation. Fish meal is also another safe option in the rare instances when iron is inadequate.

Do *not* buy preparations where the products has been chelated, it seems that this does not suit the alimentary tract of any animal. Cases have come up where stock on predominantly chelated minerals have been at great risk from liver damage and failure. It does not happen with minerals in their basic form. I guess that receiving chelation by mouth does not really occur in nature.

Proprietary Licks — Bullets and Boluses or Not?

Various authorities have pointed out the uselessness of proprietary salt licks and blocks, as they never contain enough of the minerals that are really needed. On-farm supplementation according to soil analyses is suggested as the most economical method for correcting herd health problems. The lick mixture provided above has proved successful with sheep of all ages, once they can be persuaded to take it (this is why I emphasize that young sheep should be trained to taking feed or licks). Occasionally additions as per the analysis have to be made.

A disturbing finding in several research papers recently is that bullets for various mineral deficiencies do not always work as they should. In smaller ruminants both bullet and scratcher (this is the piece of metal inserted at the same time as the bullet, which periodically scratches the bullet and releases some of its contents) have been found at post mortem to be coated with calcium, and therefore the contents have become unobtainable. Cobalt bullets have been mentioned especially. If you are using this method make sure, by taking blood counts regularly if necessary, that they are working. I still favor the method above and using a lick.

Bone-Building Minerals

In the 1960s I attended a lecture where the ecologist Peter Bennet first showed the deformed skeletons of sheep. I realized then just how much trouble can be caused by the lack of bone-building minerals. Sheep are no good unless they have sound bones, and especially teeth. It must be remembered that four minerals and two vitamins are the bare essentials for healthy bones — and I am sure when we know more there will be others as well. The minerals are calcium and magnesium, which are found naturally in dolomite; copper and boron, which are found naturally in seaweed meal and as copper sulfate and sodium borate (borax). An article in the May 2003 issue (page 138) of the *Townsend Letter for Doctors* emphasizes that boron is needed in the body for magnesium to be correctly absorbed. Vitamins A and D, both found naturally in cod-liver oil, must also be given to the sheep for the whole thing to work properly.

The lick already mentioned and as above must be kept dry. It is particularly important to keep it always available. It will tide the sheep over until the paddock health is improved, and even more importantly during times of stress and drought; and particularly after drought when the first green comes away. I would hate to think how often I have seen people cease hand feeding and bothering about licks the moment the first green grass appeared after a long dry spell with, of course, very nasty results.

Boron (Sodium Borate)

Boron is extremely important in the cultivation of nut trees and all legumes, alfalfa will not grow or produce nodules in a boron (or calcium and magnesium) deficient field. In serious cases of deficiency the plants will reach a height of about eight inches and then just die off. Root vegetables can also be affected, particularly turnips, they will be black in their centers and fail to grow. In wheat, boron deficiencies are every easy to monitor — if it has not been done previously from an analysis, which would be the best way. When boron is deficient, the wheat heads do not fill properly, a wheat head fattens first in the center, next at the head and third (if boron is adequate) at the base.

For sheep this is an essential trace mineral needed in very small amounts. Calcium and magnesium will not be correctly utilized if boron is missing, leading to problems associated with deficiencies of these minerals such as rickets, bone malformations and, in particular, arthritis. It is necessary to have soil analyses that monitor boron — in Australia there are areas where it is deficient and arthritis in all animals (and humans) is widespread. This is usually controlled by feeding either seaweed products, which contain natural boron, or if that is not enough, as was the case in my milking goat herd, I had to add one gram per head of borax every week. Until this was done, the creaking joints were audible as the goats walked around the fields. Ten years later we find that the dose has to be doubled — sadly, the deterioration of the soil seems to speed up as the years go by.

If the soil analysis showed boron at .2 or lower, I would advise adding about 20 grams to the full lick, this would have to be mixed in very well indeed. Boron was removed from the poison list in Australia a few years ago and it should not have been on it (it may not have been on such a list in the United States). It is now realized how essential this mineral is for bone health and also for the health of the brain.

Calcium

Calcium is required for the nervous and muscular systems, normal heart function and blood coagulation. It is also needed for bone growth. However calcium must *always* be considered in conjunction with magnesium because the two minerals interact and must be kept in balance at all times. An excess of calcium will cause magnesium to be depleted and vice versa. It is therefore unwise to feed calcium carbonate (ground limestone) or dicalcium phosphate (DCP), as these cause a depletion of magnesium. Where magnesium is very high in the soil, the blood should be monitored to check if the levels are correct.

The correct blood ratios are 2.4 ml per liter blood serum of calcium, with magnesium and phosphorus both just under half that amount. In the United States where magnesium is often excessively high, ground limestone could be substituted for one-third of the dolomite in the lick. If hand feeding, dolomite, which contains both minerals, should still be used because feed is quite often grown with superphosphate, which ties up magnesium, or grown on magnesium deficient ground, or both. Florida and a line running up the middle of the United States, and around the Ozarks are mapped low in magnesium, which is unusual for the country.

A headline in an English farming magazine of several years ago read: "Excess Calcium Gives Cows (Or Sheep) Mastitis." This statement is not strictly correct. Calcium does not cause mastitis, but by depleting magnesium, which is needed to maintain udder health, an imbalance is created. Mastitis organisms were then able to gain entry and proliferate. Mastitis is *very* uneconomic in farmed sheep and even more so in milking sheep.

Excess calcium both in the plant and animal world is linked with a weakening of the cell structure and lowering of immunity to disease, especially of viral origin. Dr. Neville Suttle of Moredun Research Institute in Edinburgh also emphasizes "that feeding an excess of minerals like calcium can do more harm than good, predisposing to milk fever."

Calcium should be found in all feeds and alfalfa in particular, if well grown without irrigation, is a good source; this is why dryland alfalfa grown on remineralized soil is good (i.e., without artificials). However, its presence depends on two factors:

1. That the original soil where the feed was grown
   contained adequate levels of calcium (and boron).
2. Whether artificial fertilizers were used — these
   reduce the levels of available minerals in the feed.

In ideal conditions, alfalfa roots have been found to go down fourteen feet and collect a great many useful minerals on the way; however, when heavily irrigated and grown with artificials the roots stay near the surface just waiting for the next hit of junk food and water.

Conditions caused by lack of calcium are arthritis, uneven bone growth, knock-knees, cow hocks, poor muscle tone leading to prolapse, poor teeth, a general lack of well-being and susceptibility to cold and therefore respiratory problems. Calcium and magnesium deficiencies will also cause lactation problems such as milk fever, mastitis, low milk production and high somatic cell count.

Calcium in these situations is best supplied as in dolomite, even in areas where the magnesium is reasonably high. For prolapse and associated disorders, the best type of calcium to use is calcium fluoride, which is obtainable as cell salts from most health shops and has nothing to do with sodium fluoride. This disorder is fairly rare so the remedy is quite economical to use. Give a sheep the recommended human dose for a day or two, that is usually enough. Should an imbalance of calcium and magnesium be suspected, a soil analysis *must* be done. There are odd pockets where magnesium is higher than calcium, so the levels present must be known. For permanent feeding, if calcium on its own is needed, ground limestone (calcium carbonate) should be given. The source of this and the analysis on the bag of calcium carbonate should be checked. Some quarries produce an article which has 9 percent magnesium in it, and it is therefore more correctly dolomite.

It is important to remember that calcium (and magnesium) assimilation depend on adequate boron, copper and vitamins A and D in the diet. (See above regarding boron.) Vitamins A and D (cod-liver oil) should be available from the sunlight and well-grown feed, otherwise they will have to be given as a drench or injection.

As has been noted in earlier chapters, calcium is essential in the ground in the correct ratio. Neal Kinsey notes that calcium helps the soil to flocculate freely and improves the texture. No crop, tree, grain or pasture will grow as it should if calcium is too low.

Magnesium

Magnesium deficiency appears to be rapidly becoming the biggest problem in modern conventional farming worldwide, possibly even in the United States where it is almost universally high (except for Florida, and the regions mentioned above). In the United Kingdom, magnesium deficiencies as we know them in Australia did not occur before chemical fertilizers came into common use; now deficiencies appear to be rife in livestock of all kinds. Magnesium is more readily inhibited by artificial fertilizers than calcium. Early experiments by Peter Bennet indicated that two bags of superphosphate inhibited the uptake of 10 pounds of magnesium to the acre.

In Australia most soils were originally deficient in magnesium once the fertile top soil, which apparently held a good amount of organic matter, had been used up or eroded. The country missed the last Ice Age, unlike the United States, and the minerals have never really built up as they have done in other parts of the world.

Considerable leaching of all minerals takes place in high rainfall areas as well. Both magnesium and calcium are rendered inert in the body by the sodium fluoride used in our water supplies. This must be considered if animals are drinking water containing fluoride salts. Magnesium is needed for all enzymes, both gut and muscle, to function correctly. This information should be especially noted for those running small flocks of specialist sheep in or near urban areas — if they are on reticulated water.

I think the fact that magnesium helps the enzymes to function properly explains why so many farmers have told me that they felt dolomite in the feed had improved their feed conversion rate. Magnesium, as it assists the enzymes in their functions, also makes mastitis and acetonemia in milking animals a thing of the past.

Seventy percent of ingested magnesium is needed for bone growth, the remaining 30 percent for neuromuscular transmission, muscular health and a healthy enzyme and nervous system. The section on calcium shows how magnesium can be depressed by an excess of that mineral. It is also almost totally removed from the system by feeds high in nitrates, such as capeweed, variegated thistle and some broad-leaved plants. Animals grazing capeweed (see end of Chapter 5) must have dolomite added to their ration. Sheep particularly will succumb to scouring and general debility in the first instance and iodine deficiency in the second, followed by a fairly rapid death. After the 1983-1984 drought, one of the most serious in Australia up to that time, hundreds of sheep (and cattle) died in Northern Victoria from this cause.

Conditions caused by a deficiency of magnesium (with calcium) include grass, lactation and travel tetanies, mastitis, acetonemia, arthritis, founder, warts (the virus that causes these prefers a magnesium deficient host), uneven bone growth as well as most of the conditions related to calcium deficiency.

Stock whose bones have shown abnormal growth patterns or changes have been much improved in a few months by supplementation of dolomite. Deformed jaws and crooked legs are very rarely congenital. From cases seen it appears that it is seldom too late (or too early) to reverse it by properly supplemented feeding.

Excessively nervous behavior is also attributable to a lack of magnesium. Many animals have become much easier to manage when dolomite has been added to their rations, changing from excitable to quite calm individuals in a matter of hours or days.

It should be remembered that overdosing with calcium and magnesium can lead to depletion of trace minerals and iodine. However, if oral copper poisoning is suspected (as from heliotrope, St. John's wort or Patterson's Curse — all copper-bearing plants) dolomite with vitamin C, as sodium ascorbate, can be used quite successfully as an antidote.

Magnesium should normally be obtained from feed grown in soils containing adequate levels of the mineral. Unfortunately, this is rarely the case as most feed is grown using artificial fertilizers and/or on depleted land. In Australia there is another source of calcium and magnesium for those lucky enough to live in the right areas — the artesian bore. Analyzing the water would be the best method of finding out what minerals a bore contains. They can vary immensely, even in the same district and can also, sadly nowadays, be contaminated with spray and nitrate residues, just as they often are in the United States. Dolomitic lime, if it is of a decent quality, which means a ratio of about 45 ppm calcium to 36 ppm magnesium, is the safest way of providing these minerals, whether in the feed, licks or as a top dressing.

Most of the remarks applicable to calcium in agriculture apply to magnesium. It *must* be supplied with calcium in the correct ratios for fully healthy plant growth. One factor should be borne in mind, monitor the soil for magnesium deficiencies and not the plant; a plant tissue test can show up a magnesium deficiency when there is adequate amounts in the soil. As far as a plant is concerned too much and too little show the same signs, this is according to Neal Kinsey's writings, talks and tapes.

Plants that cause magnesium deficiencies in stock are Capeweed *(Arctotheca calendula)* and Smooth Cat's Ear *(Hypochoeris glabra)*. These plants can be taken as an indication of a paddock's low status in magnesium and usually calcium as well.

Note: Lack of magnesium absorption can be due to a shortfall of boron in the soil as one needs the other. Another reason for having a good soil audit *(Townsend Letter for Doctors*, May 2003, page 136).

Cobalt

Cobalt is needed for healthy bone development and for the health of red blood cells. Cobalt anemia causes persistent ill-thrift, depleted appetite, susceptibility to cold and death — this condition is sometimes referred to as swayback or coast disease in Australia. It is a fast and potent killer although it is quite reversible. It can actually occur in any livestock, even horses, but sheep are the most susceptible.

The first sign of a shortfall is unhappiness, followed by lack of appetite, scouring, wasting and death in about 70 hours if nothing is done. The initial diagnostic tool, as soon as a sheep is seen to be off-color, is to take its temperature. If it is short of cobalt the temperature will be sub-normal. Feeling a sheep's ears is a good indication as the ears will feel really cold even on the hottest days if the temperature is subnormal. Again, this highlights the importance of having the soil analyzed by a firm that includes a cobalt readout. The information on cobalt levels is too important to depend on learning from a dead sheep.

Causes of cobalt deficiency are often low pH and acidity; but there are high pH districts where it just appears to be missing. Possibly any pH right outside the normal range can inhibit the presence of the mineral as does overuse of artificial fertilizers. Original deficiencies are fairly rare. On a very poor farm where all those conditions applied; after analyzing and top-dressing with one ton of dolomite to the acre, the cobalt was back in the food chain in about 15 months.

Cobalt is synthesized into vitamin B12 in the gut and this synthesis can cease to work in cases of extra stress, illness or the administration of drugs. When this happens the *only* way to reactivate the synthesis is to inject vitamin B12, oral administration will *not* work. This is a water-soluble injection which is completely safe, the body merely excretes any administered in excess of requirements. Sheep need two to three ml according to size and if you are using B12 as a routine injection make sure that the mixture contains 1,000 mg to a ml.

In March 1998 I did a talk to farmers at Reedy Creek, South Australia, they are using cobalt sulfate far in excess of the amounts advised above. On the basis of their administration of the mineral I would suggest, for these kind of conditions, that a pound of cobalt can be added to the normal lick mixture given at the head of this chapter. That is still below the amount that the farmers on that particular part of Australia are feeding (apparently quite successfully) to their sheep. (See next chapter, section on vitamin B12, for further information.)

The general rule is that cobalt sulfate is extremely toxic and expensive and should only be given at a rate of three grams between 40 sheep per day. Extra amounts of cobalt sulfate should only be prescribed by a vet. Feeding seaweed meal ad lib will help because seaweed contains all minerals in a natural form. Seaweed is often enough to correct slight problems. If the land is cobalt deficient, the best course is to have this amended by remineralizing (see this and previous chapters) with the required lime minerals. Consult Chapter 6 on soil deficiencies. It is particularly important to make sure any analyst who tests the farm's soil includes cobalt (for some unknown reason this is quite often omitted). Copper deficiencies are serious, but far more so if cobalt is also missing.

Copper

This is a mineral which can be top-dressed in areas where copper deficiencies are a big problem and the calcium pH is above 5.8. A printout in *Acres U.S.A.* some years ago told of farmers near Goyders Lagoon in central Australia in the 1940s. Their sheep had become virtually unproductive due to what we now know are deficiencies of copper affecting the wool and also causing lack of estrus. There was just enough copper in their systems to keep them moderately healthy and that was all. The land (which had a high pH) was top-dressed with straight copper sulfate and the district never looked back. This can only be done on a high pH without the risk of losing the material spread (any pH under 5.8 calcium is too low to topdress with straight trace minerals as they are sulfated out by the first shower of rain — I learned that the hard way.

I prefer to tell farmers to have the lick given in Chapter 5 and above available at all times. The farmers have reported huge improvements in their wool checks and sheep health when they do. Occasionally in animals that are not used to hand feeding some encouragement in the form of spreading a little grain on the top of the lick is necessary to get them started. They take what they need, when they need it — once they know it is there.

Neal Kinsey says that rust in crops occurs on copper deficient soils, again a case of pulling the soil back into the correct balance so that the copper is available or adding it to the soil if the pH is high enough. Copper is inhibited when pH is either too low or too high, the latter effect is worse in droughts. When I was investigating why copper shortfalls were so great, a researcher at Monash who was studying the mineral told me that copper is inhibited virtually 100 percent by superphosphate, so putting out super and copper is not an option. Getting the soil into balance is. The great French veterinarian and researcher André Voisin, who is the father of cell grazing, states in his seminal book, *Soil, Grass and Cancer,* that nitrogenous fertilizers of any kind *all* tie up or inhibit copper 100 percent. These effects must account for many deficient animals.

In Australia and possibly the United States, there are three so-called weeds, which all have blue flowers, that carry copper in amounts large enough to kill light colored sheep if they are driven to eating them by hunger although the dark-colored animals do very well. A rough rule of thumb is that most blue flowered plants are high in the mineral. Black faces and legs make a remarkable difference in copper requirements. The plants are: St. John's wort *(Hypericum perforatum),* Patterson's Curse *(Echium plantagineum),* both deeply rooted plants that proliferate in a copper deficient top soil in Australia. These plants are probably nature's answer to replacing copper near the surface. The third plant, Heliotrope *(Heliotropium amplexicaule)* is a shallow-rooted annual that grows to excess in soils low in calcium and magnesium but containing adequate copper. It causes stock to die of jaundice (commonly called the yellows) as do the other two, and deaths from all three can be stopped if the stock have licks available that contain plain dolomite.

In the body of the sheep copper is needed for optimum health, resistance to disease including coccidia, enzootic ataxia, healthy bone growth and internal parasites of *all* kinds. Tapeworm and liver fluke especially are susceptible to even quite small amounts of copper. It is needed against all diseases of fungal origin and especially for a healthy immune system. Failure to come into estrus (season) regularly is possibly the most uneconomic effect of low copper from a financial point of view. Sheep whose copper levels are right cycle regularly at the correct time. Andre Voisin, the French researcher and veterinarian, states categorically that cancer is a result of too little copper in the diet. Footrot, cowpox, dermatitis (when the fleece looks and feels like steel wool), ringworm, foot scald, proud flesh (which often occurs in bad cases of footrot as well), Johne's disease (Crohn's), brucellosis (when deficiencies of iodine, manganese and cobalt are also present), poor fleece quality (tender wool), animals that chew fences and bark and dark animals which are off-color are suffering from lack of copper. This is why old-time shepherds always kept a black sheep with their flocks, on occasion they would go quite white and sometimes just striped, indicating a deficiency. My daughter, who is a wool classer, brought me a section from a black fleece where the standard lick was removed from the paddock one month before shearing. The wool nearest the skin was pale grey for half an inch.

Another very serious effect of a copper shortfall is anemia, especially in Australia where most soils have adequate iron, but without copper iron *cannot* be utilized. Given the fact that iron tonics are undesirable at the best of times due to iron's depressing effect on vitamin E, seeing the stock get the correct amount of copper in their rations or licks is the obvious answer. Do not be led astray by the enormous amounts of iron tonics offered on sale in fodder stores, they do not deal with the cause of the anemia, and they inhibit vitamin E (see section on that vitamin).

The lick above is a balanced mix that has been tested and used on sheep of all ages and types; weaners especially go for it. With milk sheep it could be mixed with the bail feed at the rate of two grams per head per day.

Research carried out in Japan in the 1960s with humans showed that black-haired people needed nearly six times more copper than fair-haired individuals. I have found those ratios to be right in dark and light-colored animals. As mentioned earlier, this is why the shepherds kept black animals as a monitor.

On our Gippsland farm where the cobalt came back into the food chain in 18 months, iron levels in the soil were 1,600 times the desirable levels. After two months the stock were dying of anemia and were riddled with liver fluke. Raising the copper in the ration cured the anemia and the fluke in ten days. In other words, animals were then able to use as much of the iron as they needed. Hungerford in his *Diseases of Livestock* says that repeated and unexplained scouring is often caused by a lack of copper. The first time we tested this was with Merino weaners on a farm in northern Victoria; they had been scouring for weeks. I suggested the farmer make up a mix of two parts dolomite to one part copper, run the sheep through the race and put a teaspoon (three grams) of the mixture straight into their mouths. The scouring ceased by the end of the day. Nowadays I do not advocate that course of action as putting the sheep on the lick is safer. Many farmers who have habitually drenched their animals on chemical drenches at certain times of year have a problem with not doing it. When the sheep are on the lick already mentioned they do *not* need supplementary drenching, especially since this is generally with substances that are not found in nature.

Occasionally stock will show the classic "spectacles" appearance when copper deficient; the skin around the eyes appearing dry, light colored and pulled away, making the animal look as though it is wearing spectacles; I do not think this would show up in white sheep, but it apparently does in black ones. Readers of the Herriot veterinary books will remember an instance where some calves were dying, and Herriot suddenly noticed the spectacles, supplemented them with copper and all was well.

Copper, like most minerals, is highly toxic in excess and does not taste nice to humans at all, although I have spoken to number of people (of very fine physique) who regularly had it given to them as children (in cod-liver oil). Zinc in excess suppresses copper, but it appears that the reverse, according to a researcher with whom I have discussed this, does not occur (Pickering). I have also observed this fact in the field.

Too much copper kills, but too little does just the same. If copper is always fed in conjunction with dolomite and in the ratios mentioned in the lick, the mixture can be fed in those proportions when hand feeding as well — approximately four grams a week to a sheep. There have been no signs of intoxication with this method. Copper injections should be avoided because an overdose cannot be treated, the same applies to using copper carbonate (see below). If too much copper is ingested orally, dolomite, sodium ascorbate (vitamin C) powder orally, and vitamin B15 injections together produce a quick cure. In serious cases the addition of activated charcoal will also help. Copper toxicity shows up as an acute liver attack though the liver is a very easy organ to re-activate.

Copper sulfate *only* should be fed to stock, never copper carbonate. Copper carbonate is twice as strong as the sulfate in the body and is not so easily lost. Therefore an overdose could easily be fatal. At the request of a copper researcher I fed copper carbonate to my animals for four months, carefully halving the amounts. The exercise was not a success, both horses and goats did much better on the sulfate variety of copper and there is at least room for error if there is an overdose while there is no room for error with the carbonate.

Seaweed meal (kelp) contains a significant amount of copper, and very often providing it in the lick or ad lib helps to offset small shortfalls. This is especially true in English type sheep whose copper requirement is nowhere near as high as that of Merinos (see the beginning of this chapter).

Iodine

Many countries in the world now appear to be iodine deficient, surprisingly even in coastal areas. Sixty or seventy years ago in the Northern Hemisphere, buying food grown near the sea provided enough iodine for the inland sheep to receive what they needed. This is no longer the case. I suspect that NPK fertilizer use may have something to do with this.

Iodine is not truly a mineral and thus cannot figure on an analysis. It is absolutely essential for the health of the thyroid gland, which controls the health of all the glands in the whole body — no thyroid, no life. In extremes of weather the body's rate of iodine excretion is higher, and it will be noticed that sheep who have ad lib access to kelp meal will take large amounts when there is a sudden burst of cold or very hot weather. Therefore, if an animal is iodine deficient, no matter what minerals or vitamins it is given, they will not be assimilated properly until the iodine requirements are met. Fortunately, the requirement is not very high, and the addition of the lick or offering ad lib kelp is usually enough to meet it. This is preferable to using inorganic iodine in the form of potassium iodide or Lugol's solution. Both are toxic in excess as well as being expensive. A vet will advise on alternate forms of iodine supplementation if necessary.

If there is an iodine shortfall, obviously the animal's system cannot function properly and this should be considered as a possible basis of any problem. As seaweed supplementation has become the norm in all stock feeding worldwide nowadays, deficiencies should be unlikely; seaweed provides a huge spectrum of minerals in their most natural and assimilable form.

Signs of an iodine deficiency — or excess — are, in severe cases, a swollen goiter and in mild form dandruff or scurf, in wool sheep the latter shows up as a yellow yoke near the skin and, of course, in either case sub-normal health. It *must* be remembered that the signs of iodine excess and deficiency are identical; if newly purchased stock exhibits any of these signs make the kelp available on free choice, do not force them to eat it. If they have too much already in their systems, forcing them to eat it could lead to severe trouble. Note: the goiter is the hard piece in the middle of the throat, salivary glands are each side of the goiter and, if swollen, are often mistaken for goiter but are *quite* different, they are soft and usually the sign of an infection of some kind.

A potent and common cause of iodine deficiency is overfeeding of legumes such as alfalfa, clovers, lupins, beans, peas, soy products, lucerne trees (tagasaste), tree lupins, etc. These are termed goitrogenic feeds, because in extreme cases they cause the goitre to swell. Feeding too many legumes will cause a preponderance of ram lambs. The female fetus has the greatest need for iodine. If there is a deficiency, she does not develop and is probably reabsorbed. It is also possible in some cases that females are not even conceived. Occasionally in iodine-deficient sheep, strong ram lambs are born — but the ewe lambs may be weak, dying and hairless. A fluoridated water supply will also depress iodine.

Feeds high in nitrates like capeweed and many other broadleaved "weeds," when present in large amounts (such as after a drought, especially on unhealthy soil), can also inhibit iodine and cause thyroid dysfunction. If animals are in fields that are largely growing capeweed or similar, iodine supplementation is necessary as is dolomite (see magnesium section). Again, seaweed meal would usually be enough and should be mixed half in half with the dolomite.

Remember that an iodine deficiency should always be considered as the base cause of practically every problem. A blood test will show up a large iodine deficiency, but might not highlight a chronic mild shortfall. The lick at the head of this chapter would be adequate, so would a good liquid kelp supplement that contains *no* extras, and *no* chelated minerals. The minerals in kelp are naturally chelated, human-made minerals are not needed and can damage the liver.

Iron

Many minerally depleted soils are often left with high iron and salt, both often too plentiful. This is commonly found even in soils which are basically good, even in volcanic country. It is also often the only mineral left after extended use of artificials. A farm we bought in eastern Australia where iron was 1,600 times too high, and everything else except the salt (600 times too high) was extremely low, partly inhibited by the high iron. When, following an Albrecht-type analysis, the correct amount of lime minerals — dolomite in this case — one ton to the acre were applied, the fields were soon showing marked signs of improvement.

Potassium and vitamin E are the major casualties of high iron as a rule. In the body iron destroys the vitamin E, which is why iron tonics must be avoided as far as possible. As above, this situation can be amended quite easily by top-dressing the area after a soil analysis. Bringing the calcium/magnesium up to the correct level is usually all that is needed to bring the iron levels back into balance.

The most important fact to remember about iron is that without copper it *cannot* be assimilated, and many so called iron deficiencies are merely due to a copper shortfall. Iron is necessary for the health of the red blood cells, and therefore for the general wellbeing of the whole herd.

As mentioned in the section on copper, in spite of the prevalence of iron, anemia would be one of the biggest causes of sickness in stock. Vitamin B12 injections can be used in the short term until the copper in the lick or ration comes into play. It will help raise iron levels very quickly and not have the great disadvantage of totally suppressing vitamin E as dosing with inorganic iron does. Feeding fish meal is a good way to raise iron in stock should there be problems, fish products are totally beneficial and of course safe, unlike meat products (see Appendix).

Both iron and cobalt are synthesized into vitamin B12 in the gut, and injections of the latter can be used in severe iron (and cobalt) anemia cases. If there is a lack of iron in the fields, top-dressing with basic slag, a by-product of the iron smelting industry used to be used, but is not usually a permitted input in organic set-ups. This practice was quite usual in Europe and the United States, and was generally done every six years by conventional farmers.

Molybdenum

This element is needed for maximum fertility. A deficiency can occur in land that is exhausted and low in organic matter, specially if the pH is below 5.0. However high levels of the mineral are dangerous and can be an indirect cause of anemia (by affecting copper and cobalt utilization). This is probably the reason why we were taught to adjust the levels of the other elements through top-dressing and raising the lime minerals to their correct level rather than altering the molybdenum. Increasing the organic matter is really the best way to adjust this problem. There are areas in Australia where the molybdenum levels are rising due to fallout from some of the industrial complexes. The vets who first drew my attention to this about 20 years ago were extremely worried about the situation. Always check molybdenum levels in all coal products. Some have been dangerously high, and given molybdenum's role in tying up copper this is serious.

Coal dust can be a good fertilizer, but always make sure that molybdenum is included in the readout of the contents, and is not over supplied.

We had considerable trouble on a farm in northern Britain where molybdenum had been overused; the ongoing copper and cobalt deficiencies were horrific and it took about three years of very hard work to get the fields back in balance.

Phosphorus

When taking a soil analysis always insist that the total locked-up phosphorus is monitored at the same time. This mineral is essential for healthy growth and life. It should be kept in balance with calcium and magnesium, otherwise an excess of phosphorus will lead to bone fragility and many other problems of the kind associated with calcium and magnesium deficiencies. One of the problems associated with excess phosphorus is sheep (or anything else) developing cystic ovaries; in sheep this is uneconomic, although in cattle it can be manually reversed.

Phosphorus will not be lacking in healthy, well-farmed soils where organic matter and humus are in balance. Soils that have been heavily cropped with nothing returned to the soil will eventually be lacking in organic matter and a test will show if the phosphorus is missing too. I have not yet seen an analysis where locked-up (total) phosphorus was missing. Sometimes it is present in startlingly high amounts.

Artificial phosphorus, as in superphosphate or any other kind of phosphorus, was originally used in Australia as a replacement for the animal manures that had been obtainable in the Northern Hemisphere. There the stock in most places are yarded over winter and the resulting manure was spread on the paddocks to grow the next crops; this happens in the spring when any sort of stock come back out into the fields again. In autumn the required (as per analysis) lime minerals are spread. This maintained the soil balance because without the lime, the phosphorus from the organic manure could not be fully utilized. Unfortunately that rule was long-forgotten, until Dr. William A. Albrecht and Neal Kinsey reminded us.

Justus von Liebig's theories can be found in Julius Hensel's book, *Bread from Stones* (published by Acres U.S.A.). It was the addition of sulfuric acid to the guano from Nauru (in the case of Australia) that created a fertilizer that worked too quickly and the rest is history. This has reduced the quality of the soils over the years. When superphosphate was first used here, it was suggested — possibly by the people who made it, but history does not relate — that forty years would be the maximum time before soil degradation set in. It was also suggested that superphosphate should always be used in conjunction with lime, much in the same manner as the animal manures in the old days. Neither warning was heeded and now superphosphate has been used for over a hundred years in some cases with no reference to the calcium and magnesium balance of the soils. This has lead to a situation where the excessive use of phosphatic fertilizers has locked up a large range of minerals. These include magnesium, sulfur, copper, selenium, cobalt, boron, and zinc, and in some cases quite definitely phosphorus itself.

The unavailability of these valuable minerals and trace minerals has meant a huge toll in animal health. Possibly the lack of magnesium and copper being the most damaging and reading the sections on these two minerals alone will make people realize the price we are paying for overuse of phosphatic fertilizers, which are spread without referring to the important lime minerals at the same time.

Only since early 1996 have our soil analyses been showing total locked-up phosphorus, and the figures have been somewhat startling. Some dairy farms whose available phosphorus was about one-half to three-quarters of what it should have been — 10 to 15 ppm instead of 20 ppm — have from 500 to 2,800 ppm locked-up phosphorus. These "banks" will become available as the calcium/magnesium balances in the soils are corrected, so for the foreseeable future there is apparently plenty of phosphorus. As long as high numbers of dairy cattle are running, the supply of manure, and therefore the phosphorus, is virtually inexhaustible.

Phosphorus deficiencies in stock appear to be fairly rare. Even when soil levels are extremely low, the situation where the stock are disadvantaged by the low levels does not seem to arise provided all stock have access to the minerals they need, either in licks, bail feeding or hand supplementation.

There are many tales of the disasters with livestock following the use of phosphatic fertilizers; one I heard only very recently. A farmer who always killed his own mutton, before the days of refrigeration, found he could never keep it more than two or three days even in winter. Like everyone else, he used superphosphate. He either ran out of money or decided to have a change and stopped spreading it. The first change that he noticed was that the meat, properly hung as before, lasted for a couple of weeks.

I acquired a book a few years back that was written in 1920 and called *Modern Manufacture of Chemical Manures*. It was published by Sturtevant Engineering in London. I learned that one ton of phosphate rock broken down with one ton of sulfuric acid is required to make superphosphate.

Potassium (Potash)

On a farm where the potassium and sodium are out balance there is always trouble of some kind with the livestock and generally with the pasture and crops as well. (Professor Kervran explains the link between the two in his book *Biological Transmutations*).

A sheep farmer rang me five years ago saying his sheep were consuming about six pounds of salt per head. His farm was a disaster area, with too many chemicals and artificials, low pH, etc. I suggested that he unroll one of the big round bales of hay (equal to about 36 of the old-fashioned small bales), put a 16 gallon container of unpasteurized cider vinegar (in Australia it is quadruple strength) into his fire pump full of water (about 500 gallons), and water the hay with it. I suggested he do this for about three weeks running. The sheep stopped punishing the salt from the first day. Salt and potassium interchange.

Potash is absolutely essential for all life, both plant and animal. It is rapidly being lost worldwide due to chemical farming. In the Haughley experiment it was proven that potash was the mineral most affected by artificials, and, in spite of being replaced with muriate or sulphate of potash, was quite steadily lost. On land that was being farmed naturally it was found to be self-renewing with no danger of running out. On poor, low-pH soils potassium is inhibited by high iron as well as the acidity.

According to Charlotte Auerbach's book, *The Science of Genetics*, a lack of potassium and vitamin C at conception can interfere with the true pattern of inheritance. So when breeding valuable stock, it is essential that the paddocks be as healthy as possible.

Possibly the most serious result of a potassium deficiency is difficult births (dystokia). Having to pull every lamb is *not* desirable; it is too hard on the lamb and the ewe to say nothing of the farmer. In the short term, cider vinegar contains enough potassium to enable all stock to have their young naturally, but raising the health of the paddocks is the best long-term solution. A vet from the Western District of Victoria told me that in the 1965 drought he had to pull 95 percent of all the calves in his area. There was no green feed and he considered that a potassium deficiency was the cause, and we know now that he was right; chemical-free green feed is needed to supply the mineral.

A potassium deficiency causes constriction of the blood vessels in areas of the body where they are fairly fine — in the extremities — hence navicular disease in horses and repetitive strain injury (RSI) in human beings; both respond to potassium supplementation either by tablets or extra cider vinegar. Dystokia seems to be caused by a lack of blood supply to the uterus and cervix in the final stages of pregnancy. In a normal, healthy pregnancy the fetus moves constantly, until such time as it is presented in the birth canal in the right position, and the birth takes place hassle free. When potassium is lacking the fetus is locked in position, and, speaking as one who has pulled an inordinate numbers of other farmers' lambs, it is virtually immovable. Extracting it can be damaging to both mother and offspring.

Potassium must be in balance with both magnesium and sodium in the body and the soil.

Sodium

Too much salt kills just as easily as an excess of any other mineral. Sodium must be in balance with potassium in the soil, but all too often it is in excess, especially if sodic fertilizers such as artificial potash have been used. Real salt that has not been purified should contain a fair spectrum of beneficial minerals. Most salt as prepared for human consumption is overprocessed, denatured and is *not* a good food — therefore it should not be fed to sheep or any other animal.

Salt is essential for life, but in our civilization — due to sodic fertilizers, poor soil and bad irrigation practices — there is generally far too much of it already in the food chain. This applies to animals as well, and nearly all proprietary preparations, licks or whatever, contain excess sodium. Salt should always be available to stock of any kind, especially sheep, in as basic a form as possible. Rock salt in lumps and not broken up is ideal and does not suffer much rain damage if left out.

Too much salt can depress potassium (see section above), cause edema (fluid retention), cancer and other degenerative conditions. It also prevents the sheep from using its fodder correctly. However, when animals have a craving for salt and eat large quantities of it they are frequently looking for potassium. As stated above, the two interchange in the body.

Years ago a doctor told me how troops in India always had to be given salt tablets. However when they were later also supplied with the some essential minerals and vitamins, the salt was able to be materially reduced in their diets. I also found this with my animals who received their required minerals and hardly, if ever, touched the salt on offer. But whenever a new beast arrived it often spent the first few days punishing the salt blocks though once the minerals from the feed came into play it, like my other animals, ignored the salt.

Artificial fertilizers have certainly contributed to salinity, but I consider poor irrigation practices to be the major culprit in the dramatic rise in salt levels. In much of Australia the salinity is manmade, although parts of South Australia (including Kangaroo Island) and West Australia do have naturally high salinity. When I had an irrigation farm I found that balancing the soils and using an aerator meant that it took only three runs of water a summer for pasture. The water went to where it was supposed to be — in the ground. The other farmers took a weekly run, and most of it went off down the nearest gully or road.

Selenium

It is doubtful whether a deficiency of selenium affects plant growth very materially, and possibly it does not figure on many soil analyses for this reason. However, there is absolutely no doubt that a shortfall can affect stock very seriously indeed — to the point of death in a great many instances.

When we first came to Australia in the late '50s, selenium deficiencies were only believed to occur in parts of the Western District of Victoria and around Canterbury in New Zealand. However, as time went on, rumors of selenium shortfalls in plenty of other places started to come in. In the middle eighties a rather cross vet friend in southeastern Australia asked me to find out what I could about the mineral as he was sure many of the stock in his practice were suffering quite severely from a deficiency. He had been definitely told by the Department of Agriculture that it was impossible as there was no record of a lack of selenium in that part of Australia. The book I got from the United States answered most of the questions, and our growing knowledge of what low pH and artificial fertilizers were doing to minerals supplied the rest of the information. We were faced with a picture that showed that a whole host of minerals were being tied up and rendered unavailable by artificial fertilizers with or without low pH. Selenium in particular was at great risk because the sulfur levels in all soils were falling dramatically, partly for the same reason. Unfortunately until the middle eighties in Australia the only firm that did a full soil analysis did not monitor sulfur, so we really did not know whether it was there or not.

Dr. Richard A. Passwater, author of *Selenium as Food and Medicine,* stated categorically that without enough sulfur in the diet to provide the amino acids in the gut, especially methionine and cystine, selenium could *not* be assimilated — it was as simple as that. The ongoing low sulfur levels in the fields were responsible for the selenium deficiencies being so serious.

Like most minerals, trace and otherwise, selenium is equally dangerous in excess or deficiency. A small amount is needed for fertility, particularly of the male, without it the sperm tend to be weak and drop their tails. The mineral is also needed for healthy muscles. White muscle disease and muscular dystrophy are conditions exacerbated by a shortage of selenium. Complete and sudden cessation of growth, with or without muscle wasting signs, could mean a selenium deficiency in all young animals.

Excess selenium can cause a malformed fetus and/or poisoning. Sodium selenite (inorganic selenium) is only obtainable through a veterinary surgeon so accidental poisonings should not occur. However, Passwater's book indicated that one mg of organic selenium (as in seaweed meal) is equal to four mg of inorganic selenium, and the seaweed (ad lib or as in the lick at the head of this chapter) should therefore be the best (and safest) method of supplementation.

Selenium is linked with vitamin E, and often giving that vitamin alone will effect a cure in mild deficiency cases. In fact this can be used as a test. If a sick sheep responds to 2,000 units of vitamin E, you can be sure that it is suffering from a selenium deficiency. The farmer can then give seaweed ad lib in the lick as already suggested and/or consult the vet for the best kind of supplementation.

Sulfur

Sulfur is both needed and used up by oilseed crops. One figure, mentioned in *Acres U.S.A.* was that a crop of canola or soy would remove 50 pounds of sulfur per hectare. It would be wise to topdress with gypsum (calcium sulfate) both before and *after* oilseed crops so that the crop grows to its full potential and the paddock would not be deficient for the next crop or pasture.

In spite of the fact that I mentioned in the section on selenium that sulfur did not figure in early soil analyses and it has been fashionable to say that our knowledge of sulfur is fairly recent, this is not really so. A booklet on sulfur put out by the CSIR in 1928 (no O in those days), "The Utilisation of Sulphur by Animals," lists all the amino acids of sulfur and their uses. CSIRO at a later date *(Rural Research Bulletin,* No. 22) did a short article on the mineral and they found that without its amino acids stock did not do well. They did not mention the onset of exterior parasites and may not have linked the two at that time. They established that as far as oral administration was concerned, as long as the sulfur did not exceed 2 percent of all fodder taken in the day, it was quite safe — a very high margin.

Keratin, whose health depends on the cystine in sulfur as well as adequate copper, is a very important constituent of wool, hair, hooves, horns, etc. It is only one of the many amino acids provided by sulfur. Protein levels also depend on amino acids of sulfur, which may perhaps explain the falling proteins in crops as the sulfur in the soil falls. Logically it could be expected that the sulfuric acid used in the manufacture of superphosphate would mean a plentiful supply of sulfur, but the reverse appears to be the case because, as mentioned in the section on selenium, sulfur levels are falling rapidly.

On the land, gypsum (calcium sulfate) is used to raise the sulfur levels where both calcium and sulfur are needed. Where high magnesium and calcium are found together, generally on high pH analyses, actual yellow sulfur can be used to help level out the magnesium and raise the sulfur levels. This situation arises more often in the United States, where high magnesium is found in much of the country. Neal Kinsey devoted quite a large section of his lectures in Australia to this very problem. He told me at that time that deficiencies of sulfur were the fastest growing problem in the United States and elsewhere as far as he could make out.

Sheep that are sulfur deficient may have lice or other exterior parasites. They will not digest their feed properly because of the link with the amino acids, especially cystine and methionine. Weaners will not progress as well as they should if sulfur is missing. The mineral is often beneficial for skin ailments, both topically (applied to the skin) as well as added to the feed, therefore skin troubles could be another sign of sulfur deficiency.

Sulfur can be added to fodder and fed to animals at any stage of development. For lice infestation at shearing, have a container of yellow dusting sulfur at hand and run a line along the back of a lousy newly shorn sheep. The amount suggested in the stock lick will maintain animals in good health and free from troublesome lodgers. In the past farmers recognized the importance of sulfur and it is often mentioned in old farming and veterinary manuals.

Zinc

Zinc is usually fairly well supplied in soil, and was originally thought to be unaffected by NPK fertilizers but is now being listed as a mineral that is starting to be affected by chemical farming. However, a 1964 a book by Karl H. Schutte states categorically that excess phosphate induces zinc deficiencies, often with unhappy results when growing grains.

Too much zinc can depress copper, and this often occurs. The reverse, which used to be believed, has been found to be untrue. Several researchers have expressed the same opinion. Certainly the tests I did with stock using very high levels indeed of copper made no difference to their zinc requirements.

Zinc is necessary for a healthy reproductive system both in males and females, particularly the former, as the prostate gland needs plenty of zinc. It is probable that there is not much difference between the requirements of the female reproductive system and that of the male, except that prostate problems are more obvious in the latter.

Facial eczema in sheep in New Zealand was a problem until it was discovered to be caused by a lack of zinc. Supplementation quickly brought it under control. The only other stock that appears to have a zinc requirement higher than that provided by seaweed are alpacas, and possibly lamas and pigs.

At some stage after 1960 a researcher incorrectly pinpointed zinc as the culprit in footrot. Copper and sulfur definitely are the answer as they are needed to keep keratin healthy. This was known and published in every veterinary manual I have seen prior to that date, going back to the early part of the century.

After selling my farm to dissolve a partnership, I rented a house in a mountain district of Victoria — surely the most deficient soil I have ever seen, even the rabbits kept away. My landlord's Merinos were in a perilous state with footrot. Five weeks before shearing they were so bad they probably would not have been able to make the shearing shed ramp. He had been feeding zinc without effect. The manager and I made up the lick already mentioned, with very high additional amounts of copper (instead of the eight pounds). It cleared them up in about a week. Zinc was not necessary. There was no sign of ill health in the few thousand that were sheared.

Zinc sulfate can be used for supplementation. It is one of the highest minerals found in seaweed, and giving kelp meal in licks or ad lib is often enough to meet the requirements of most animals. When sheep being shipped to the Middle East from Australia were dying soon after the boats left, the cause was discovered to be a zinc/potassium shortfall. This was not remedied until kelp was used as an additive. Extra amounts of zinc and potassium added to the feed had failed to remedy the situation. Minerals provided in their natural form as far as is possible appear to be far more effective than those that have been processed. Chelated minerals by mouth are not good in stock feeds, or anywhere else, for that matter.

Zinc is also indicated when recovery from sickness is not as fast as it should be — again, seaweed products will probably be all that are needed.

Chapter 9

Vitamins Need Minerals

The title of this chapter is intended to emphasize the fact that without the necessary minerals in the soil and feed, vitamins cannot perform as they should. Dr. Joel Wallach, one of the leaders in this field, has emphasized this many times and pointed out that behind every vitamin deficiency there is a mineral deficiency. I have found this to be true.

Possibly the most important single cause of vitamin deficiencies is a lack of iodine. If the thyroid gland is not working, neither will the adrenals, so vitamins cannot be synthesized. Now that the use of kelp meal forms a part of most feeding routines, much money is saved on buying vitamin supplements. Eight years ago, when I wrote the first edition of this book, persuading people to use kelp was quite a task. In the United States and Europe, feeding kelp is now considered an ongoing and permanent part of any feeding program, but, calcium, magnesium and extra copper and sulfur are also needed, especially in areas where there has been high use of NPK fertilizers. The other much-mentioned cause of vitamin (and mineral) shortfalls is chemical farming, up to 28.5 percent of all vitamins and minerals are lost in the products of chemical farming (results of the Haughley Experiment),

Note: Liquid paraffin should *never* be given internally to any animal — it destroys vitamins in the gut. If oil is needed, use a cooking variety. This was drummed into me in the late '40s and '50s, when I worked helping local vets in the United Kingdom; nowadays it seems to be largely ignored. No sick animal is going to recover if the vitamins in the gut are destroyed.

Vitamin A and Vitamin D (Retinol and Cholecarciferol)

For practical purposes these vitamins should always be considered together, which is generally where they are found in nature. Vitamins A and D from fish liver oils are in the correct natural proportions. A and D are also found in mutton bird oil. Both vitamins on their own can be dangerous, especially vitamin D, if used in excess. They are fat-soluble vitamins and so share with vitamin E and K the fact that they are not lost from the body as easily as those that are water soluble.

Vitamin A is normally stored in the liver in amounts high enough to last a sheep on a prolonged period of dry feed, approximately three to five months, but in a drought which exceeds that time, deficiencies will start to develop. Ewes that are short of vitamin A will not hold to service, or may absorb the fetus soon after. She will also be at risk for abortion, uterine and vaginal ill health. Males will be liable to get stones in the ureter and will go permanently infertile if the deficiency is serious. Should a ewe be deficient in vitamin A when the lambs are born, they will not live beyond nine days, as they will not receive enough vitamin A from the ewe to sustain life. There is also the distinct possibility that they may be born with contracted tendons (knuckle over), which is another sign of vitamin A shortfall although five ml of cod-liver oil down the throat will bring about a quick recovery. Even better, ewes should receive cod-liver oil four or five weeks before coming up to lambing to ensure that neither of the above occur.

During one of our worst droughts I was contacted by a breeder of Angora goats after the first of his two hundred does had kidded and all the kids were dead in nine days. The Department of Agriculture had referred him to me. He had 200 more does due to kid in six weeks; we were in drought, so they had not had any green pasture for about 11 months. Twenty years before I had been warned that this could happen by the head teaching vet at the University of Melbourne Veterinary Faculty; I suggested that the goat farmer give injections in this case, two injections coming up to kidding. The vitamins were usually sold as A, D and E injections, and none of the second round of kids died. It is better, however, to use the oral route unless there is an emergency as in the above example, because the injection, being oily, can set up an untidy sore on occasion.

All sheep should have feed rich in vitamin A prior to lambing. Running them on a chemical-free, remineralized green paddock can be enough to raise vitamin A levels (and this is more feasible with spring lambing). If there is any doubt, a pre-natal drench of cod-liver oil (as above) should be given and this can be mixed with liquid kelp (five to six ml of each), just make sure it has no artificially chelated vitamins added to it. Also do not put cod-liver oil in a backpack or the backpack will not be fit to use again. Cod-liver oil is very sticky and almost impossible to wash out, several 50 ml syringes are easier.

Vitamin A is particularly important for the health of the eyes and skin. An outbreak of pink eye (conjunctivitis) is a sure sign of a deficiency and so are worm infestations. A harsh dry coat and runny eyes (both signs of worms and a copper deficiency) can also be a sign of vitamin A shortfall.

A further cause of too little vitamin A has recently been reported at length in *Acres U.S.A.* in their articles on overhead power lines. This backs up my own finding with goats reared under the main grid. They appeared to have lost the ability to synthesize their own vitamin A (and D), and for three years after leaving that locality needed ongoing supplementation all year round. Another factor that can affect vitamin A levels is the use of hormones in certain processes, such as embryo transplants and similar procedures. Animals who are being used for this purpose should receive vitamin A and D regularly or they may abort and waste the whole process.

The vitamin is also susceptible to light; if an animal was left in light for 24 hours, its vitamin A reserves would be severely depleted. A period of darkness is needed to preserve the normal functioning of the vitamin and those with shedded sheep should make sure they have their lights off at night. By the same token all vitamins are destroyed by light, and should only be purchased in opaque containers.

If using a water-soluble vitamin A and D emulsion, do not add it to the water or the vitamin A may be destroyed by the light. Vitamin A is better given by drench or included in the feed where it will be eaten straight away.

If grass hay has no green color at all, one can safely assume it will not have any vitamin A either. Supplementation can be by cod-liver oil, A, D and E powder, emulsion or injections. The powder (sometimes difficult to obtain) is usually quite palatable and can be mixed with the feed, as can the emulsion or oil. Of course, the best method of supplementing with vitamin A would be by adding well-grown and harvested green feed to the diet if the sheep can be hand fed. There have been cases where conjunctivitis has been cured by merely changing afflicted stock to a paddock of organically grown and remineralized green feed.

Vitamin D (Cholecarciferol)

This vitamin is needed for bone growth and the absorption of calcium. If it is missing, disorders akin to rickets will ensue. In Europe this condition was first noted in children from the slums during the Industrial Revolution; their bones did not develop properly, and their legs started to curve from the weight of the body. It can and does happen just as readily to lambs. Even if dolomite is added to the ration, without vitamin D (and A) the calcium and magnesium are not correctly utilized. In rickets, cod-liver oil effects a cure very rapidly. Signs of vitamin D deficiency are unnatural bone formations and, in mild forms, a very harsh coat. As with vitamin A, this vitamin should be found in all properly grown green feed but the chief source of supply is sunlight, from which it is synthesized on the skin.

In areas where the sun is strongest people have naturally dark skin, which prevents them absorbing too much vitamin D as it is dangerous in excess. For this reason it should be noted that dark colored or black-faced sheep could need extra cod-liver oil, as they need more sunlight to obtain it than light-colored animals, especially if the year has been cloudy. Shedded sheep need to be monitored fairly carefully in this respect.

Vitamin B Complex

This covers a whole range of vitamins: B1, B2, B3, B5, B6, B12, B15 and biotin. Vitamin B13 (orotic acid) is not included and will only be encountered as far as I know in minerals to which it has been allied (as in magnesium orotate, etc.). Even now new vitamins are being added to the list as our knowledge of this field increases. In 1949 André Voisin was already referring to PABA as "vitamin H" (as did a 1982 edition of *Martindale),* but in Australia it is still to be found labelled as a B vitamin. These B vitamins should normally be present in all well-grown feeds, especially grains, but they may be missing if the soils in which the feeds were grown were deficient in magnesium or cobalt, which happens frequently. Milling and irradiation destroys B and other vitamins. In theory, all the B vitamins are present in B-complex powders or injections, but in practice this is not effective — it is wiser to give the specific vitamin that is needed for best results. VAM is an excellent and very effective injection, it contains vitamins, minerals and amino acids in liquid form. Give two ml VAM for a full-grown sheep, a large ram could take three ml. VAM also can be purchased as an oral paste, which is equally effective and given at the same rate of two ml for sheep.

Vitamin B1 (Thiamine)

Until a few years ago, this vitamin was hardly considered in either human or animal health; if it was, the requirement was thought to be insignificant. Now we know that it is absolutely essential and deficiencies are far more common than had previously been supposed and can be caused by feed too high in carbohydrates (a rare effect) and fungal poisoning — an only too common occurrence in feed or pastures grown on sick sour soils (see Chapter 6).

Deficiency signs vary from photosensitization and mild distress to staggering, lateral un-coordination and blindness followed by death in about 72 hours. Sheep deficient in this and other B vitamins often show scarlet streaking in the membranes of the mouth.

Thiamine is destroyed by thiaminase, which is present in some molds. This is why feed suspected of being moldy should *never* be fed to stock. Unfortunately these molds survive the pelleting process as fodder is made into mixed feeds and pellets. Do not use feeds treated thus, mass deaths have resulted.

If treatment is not started immediately death can follow in a day or two. It should be noted that these conditions only appear on pastures that are extremely poor and out of balance. The molds start in the soil organisms, because the ground is so sick, they then affect the plants and then the stock eating the pasture. Dr. William A. Albrecht explained the procedure in his usual clear manner in many articles collected in *The Albrecht Papers*.

The dose recommended for this condition is approximately eight mg of injectable vitamin B1 (obtainable from any vet or feed store) for every two pounds of body weight and this should be given by intramuscular injection every six hours until the signs disappear. One millilitre of injectable vitamin B1 should contain 126 mg — consult the bottle. Vitamin B1, like most B injections, is water soluble. This means that any excess is eliminated by the body, and there is not the danger of overdosing as there could be with an oil-based injection. Note that thiaminase poisoning is one of 200 plus diseases caused by molds and vitamin B1 may not always work. Sometimes a massive dose of vitamin C may help, but residual hormonal damage can be the result (Dr. Alenstein, DVM, *Hoard's Dairyman*). Prevention, by improving paddock health, is definitely better than cure.

Vitamin B2 (Riboflavin)

This vitamin would normally be present in well-grown green feed, it is needed for the health of the mouth and lips and for the eye's ability to withstand bright lights. Cataracts are sometimes caused by a deficiency. It is also needed in digestion. Deficiency signs could be cracks around the mouth, and a bright magenta color in the tongue or gums. Difficulty in urinating has also been noted in animals deficient in this vitamin.

Supplementation can be by crushed tablets, but a supply of really well-grown green feed or well harvested uncrushed grains should set right a deficiency fairly quickly.

Vitamin B3 (Niacin, Niacinimide, Nicotinamide, Nicotinic Acid)

Any of the above names are used to describe this vitamin, which has only recently been called vitamin B3. A deficiency is associated with mental trauma like forgetfulness and senility, neither of which is likely to affect sheep. It is however an essential part of the B complex. Fresh yeast and barley are the best sources for this vitamin.

Vitamin B5 (Pantothenic Acid, Calcium Panthonate)

All the above terms are used for this vitamin which plays an incredibly important part in a sheep's resistance to disease because it is needed for manufacturing cortisone in the adrenal cortex. Any sheep that is very ill could need vitamin B5 for recovery. Unless it has enough vitamin B5 as well as vitamin C (which sheep synthesize naturally from their feed), the manufacture of cortisone can *not* take place. Therefore the treatment of any illness caused by an infection should include extra vitamin C; usually well-grown feed would supply the vitamin B5. Ground up tablets could be used for treatment on a weight basis compared with the human intake. Injections are also sometimes obtainable. Instructions on the bottle should be followed. In the horse world a teaspoon of turmeric a week has been found to keep up the animal's supply of Vitamin B5, and it has been used very successfully (an old Chinese remedy). Sheep would need half that quantity divided up during the week if a vitamin B5 shortfall was suspected,

In the United Kingdom, pigs whose barley was replaced by maize (which provided mainly vitamin B6), suffered from a Pantothenic acid (vitamin B5) deficiency, which caused ill thrift, paralysis and death. On post mortem the symptoms resembled necrotic enteritis. Once the barley was added to the diet again there was no more trouble; this phenomenon was also noted in pigs fed maize with meat meal, linseed meal and lucerne. This highlights the advantages of feeding at least a part of barley as a supplement whenever grain is fed.

Vitamin B6 (Pyridoxine)

This B vitamin is needed for resistance to infections, particularly herpes-type infections. It is also useful as an adjunct in the treatment of nearly all infectious diseases as it helps other vitamins and minerals work better. It can be obtained in tablet form or occasionally as an injection. In humans, it must always be taken with B complex, but sheep should obtain enough of the B complex in their normal feed to make administration of B6 safe on its own (see above section). Vitamin B6 is the antidote for travel sickness in most animals and could be considered if travelling sheep to shows, etc. Give them the same dose as a human (with some extra vitamin C) for a day or two coming up to travelling. As stated above, it is found in maize (corn).

Vitamin B12 (Cyanocobalamin)

This vitamin is incredibly important on any farm. It has already been mentioned at some length in the sections on cobalt and iron, both of which are synthesized into vitamin B12 in the gut. However what is often referred to as the "intrinsic factor" is needed for these syntheses to take place, this factor ceases to operate in times of stress, use of antibiotics or sickness. B12 then *has* to be given by injection, giving B12 orally is a waste of time and money as it cannot not build up the intrinsic factor.

Deficiency signs can range from mild lassitude to serious anemic conditions, nearly always accompanied by a subnormal temperature. Coast disease (swayback) in sheep is a symptom which arises when cobalt is short. Newly born lambs that have not been able to stand up since birth are often miraculously restored to life by two ml of vitamin B12 intramuscularly. Any animal that is off its feed for no apparent reason can respond to the same treatment. As these signs often follow the administration of antibiotics or other drugs, it should be a rule that if they have to be used, the B12 must be given at the same time to offset the side effects, of which loss of appetite is often the main one. The University of Melbourne vets taught me this in the 1960s. It is also noted in Goodman and Gillman's *Pharmacological Basis of Therapeutics* that antibiotics cause this effect by making the villi in the intestines shrivel up, thus causing the guts to ache and a loss of appetite.

In cases of anemia, a course of vitamin B12 would be preferable to the administration of iron tonics with their unfortunate side effects of depressing vitamin E. The dosage, in the muscle or vein, would be two to three ml for a full-grown sheep, half that for a lamb. This is a water-soluble vitamin, and overdosing is virtually impossible.

Vitamin B15 (Pangamic Acid)

This vitamin is now available again in Australia from your vet. It is invaluable for restoring liver function and is worth using in any case of general debility or sickness. The Russians pioneered its general use 50 or more years ago, and found its main usefulness was for liver damage and gangrene. It is also a useful tool in cases of copper toxicity, which of course affects the liver — as in heliotrope poisoning, for example, or an overdose of copper sulfate. At present here this is only obtainable through your vet, who could probably be persuaded to obtain a bottle for the farm medical kit. (This is definitely used by vets in the United States. All vets that I have spoken with thought highly of it; in Australia it is sold as DADA.)

Biotin

This is another B vitamin that has suddenly come into prominence. Except for seaweed meal, it would not occur naturally in any quantity in normal concentrates unless they consisted of whole maize or beans. As always, any form of milling will remove it from grains. It is necessary for hoof and hair growth and the addition of seaweed in the licks or by drench will help restore foot health far faster than the artificial biotin in my experience.

Vitamin C (Ascorbate, Ascorbic Acid, Calcium Ascorbate, Potassium Ascorbate, Sodium Ascorbate, Zinc Ascorbate)

Vitamin C is essential for the health of the cells, strength of blood vessels, and for collagen synthesis — especially in the pads between the vertebrae and joints.

All animals (except humans, some monkeys, passiform parrots and guinea pigs) manufacture their own vitamin C in the liver from their feed. Sheep make about 15-plus grams a day, but under stress of any kind, be it trauma, sickness, travel, poison bites or whatever, the extra demand far exceeds the supply. Back in the '50s, Hungerford in his great *Diseases of Livestock* noted some "unexpected" results from the use of vitamin C and remarked that supplementation might always be worth trying. Professor Selwyn Everist also noted it could be useful for poisonings. Vitamin C can be used to control cancer, viral conditions, snake and poison bites, and as an antidote for certain poisons. It is a tremendous help in the treatment of any sickness, as it helps the body (liver and kidneys in particular) to fight back and recover.

Blood vessel fragility in all stock, which can be induced by anti-inflammatory drugs and ill health, is helped and partially prevented by vitamin C administration. Hesperidin is a part of the C complex, and it would appear to be the factor which helps strengthen blood vessels. Broken blood vessels can, of course, be the cause of blood in the milk — a serious problem in any milking operation.

Vitamin C can be given orally in feed in the form of sodium ascorbate powder, which is tasteless (ascorbic acid powder tastes sour and can also be used in feed). The former will not curdle milk and is therefore very useful when needed for sick lambs. It may also be given by injection, and is cheap and easily obtainable in 50-ml or 100-ml bottles from any good fodder merchant or vet. Only buy the brands which are two ml to the gram, there are some where it is five ml, which would mean a far higher than usually needed dose. The two ml to a gram variety is referred to throughout this book.

Sodium ascorbate powder (*not* ascorbic acid) can also be dissolved in distilled water for injection. (A teaspoon of powder makes approximately five grams, but sterile procedures *must* be used.) For intramuscular injection, sodium ascorbate is still preferable and for the intravenous route *only* sodium ascorbate can be used. In sheep, the intramuscular injection can sting slightly, this sign can be used as a yardstick to recovery because the more ill the animal is, the less it will complain *except* in the case of blackleg when any intramuscular injection given anywhere in the body except the actual blown-up leg causes extreme pain (see Chapter 10).

Vitamin C can be used in large amounts with complete safety in situations where an antibiotic might be used. Many vets use it at the same time as an antibiotic with satisfactory results. The vitamin has the great advantage that the side effects often associated with antibiotics and antivenin do not occur. When used for snake and other poison bites, it has the advantage of working slightly faster than antivenin, without the risk of anaphylactic shock. Nor does the variety of snake matter *and* the vitamin C is generally on hand — as near as the farm fridge. Sheep always seem to be bitten by snakes or taken ill at weekends or when the vet is unobtainable, so the vitamin is a useful standby. Remember that when an animal is in shock the veins collapse, so do not waste time looking for one, use the intramuscular route. Needless to say sheep will mostly be bitten on the nose unless they are just off-shears.

Nowadays many infections do not respond to antibiotics, they are only given to control secondary bacterial infections (see Chapter 10). Vitamin C, if used in sufficiently large amounts, will cure viral conditions which do not responded to normal drugs.

Zinc ascorbate has been used to cure senile cataracts, I can vouch for the fact that it stings badly in the eyes, and as my cataracts were induced by an accident with an electric fence it may not have been a fair test. Dr. W. Bellfield, DVM, and others in the United States report that small animals (and some humans) have had their cataracts dissolved using it.

Vitamin E (Tocopherol)

This is a fat-soluble vitamin, which is stored in the body under normal circumstances. It acts as an antioxidant and is a natural component of wheat germ oil. Unlike many other fat-soluble vitamins, it seems to be safe in large amounts; perhaps the requirement for it is fairly high. Vitamin E is necessary for general good health and, in particular, is useful in healing after an injury or trauma. Vitamin E has been very useful in the aftermath of pneumonia to normalize the breathing rate. It helps to heal the lesions in the lungs, 3,000 to 4,000 units would be needed daily for a sheep.

It is also helpful, with vitamin A, for fertility problems especially when allied to a selenium deficiency as vitamin E is in some way bonded with selenium. A researcher in New Zealand, a doctor, found that his pigs, which were artificially raised, suffered from a sudden death syndrome. He performed controlled experiments, supplementing one half of the piglets with vitamin E and selenium and found they lived, but the unsupplemented ones did not. Vitamin E can be used to monitor a suspected selenium deficiency; if it produces rapid favourable results, it shows that selenium is lacking and seaweed meal can be put out or the vet consulted for a short-term selenium treatment.

Vitamin E should be found naturally in seeds, unmilled grains, wheat germ and wheat bran. Fresh wheat germ oil, which should be kept refrigerated, is probably a good source for supplementation if small quantities are needed. Vitamin E is often supplied with vitamins A and D, both in powdered and injectable form, or it is obtainable on its own.

Recent research from a Colorado State University meat scientist, Gary Smith, has found that feeding (not injecting) extra vitamin E, about 100 IU a day per head for sheep, prolongs the shelf life of the meat to almost double. Apparently Australian meat is known to have higher levels of this vitamin than its American counterpart. Perhaps our feeding methods include more and better grown whole grains, which are a natural source of vitamin E. The biggest destroyers of vitamin E are iron in tonics, supplements or injections and liquid paraffin (see head of this chapter). This should be remembered at all times and, given the information in the section on iron and copper, it will be noted that it is not often necessary to supplement with iron at all as vitamin B12 usually works well. If there is severe anemia, vitamin B12 injections should be used as they do not destroy vitamin E. Fish meal can also be a source of extra iron if needed.

Vitamin H (PABA: Para Amino Benzoic Acid)

This vitamin helps the microorganisms in the gut synthesize folic acid. It can also be used to offset the effects of sunburn and sunstroke. Neither condition would normally affect sheep, except possibly genuine albinos or sheep with unpigmented skin around the eyes, which often predisposes them to skin cancer. One should not breed from animals with these defects.

Vitamin K (Menadione)

This is a fat-soluble vitamin, so it is normally stored in the body. It is needed for normal coagulation of the blood, and is therefore particularly important for all stock. The vitamin is found in grains, beans, wheat germ and well grown organic green feed, so it would seem that a deficiency should be rare. However it is very easily destroyed by mineral oil laxatives, oral antibiotics and some drugs. More importantly, it is totally destroyed by irradiation of foodstuffs. This process is becoming more common these days, and there are suggestions that irradiation may be used for grain and some packaged hay (as is sometimes used at shows). Take your own food to shows.

It is best to avoid situations that would destroy the vitamin, but if a deficiency is suspected, and bleeding where the blood failed to clot is a sign, consult your vet. Of course poisons used for rodents that stop blood clotting would need vitamin K as an antidote, but sheep are unlikely to have access to these. This vitamin has not been available up to date over the counter. Normally well grown alfalfa and green feed (grown without artificials) should contain adequate vitamin K.

Herbal and Other Useful Remedies

There are a number of excellent herbal books on the market and Juliette de Baïracli-Levy's *Herbal Handbook for Farm and Stable* is one of the best. One must remember when reading her work that all of it was done in countries where herbs grew in the pasture naturally and rainfall was on the whole regular and plentiful. This does not always happen in a continental climate where droughts can be the norm, and it did not in Australia, but the United States should be better in this respect.

This was one of the reasons that I turned to vitamins and minerals, as they *were* always obtainable when animals were off color. Maud Grieve's (often referred to simply as *Mrs. Grieve's Herbal)* is another book that I found useful, as she often gives the mineral or other make-up of the herb and one can use it in place of the actual plant. Joel Wallach and Ma Lan's *Let's Play Herbal Doctor)* is also excellent and more up to date than either of the above.

Homeopathy is also now being used quite extensively and so are Bach Flower Remedies and acupuncture; there are good books on all three — study them. Look for a vet who uses *all* modalities including drugs occasionally when necessary, although this does not need to happen too often. Below are just a few items that I have used personally and successfully with animals.

Aloe Vera

This is a plant of the cactus family that can grow naturally in most countries. Wallach lists Barbados, Cape, Curacao, Socotrana and Zanzibar aloes. Those with the actual plant often use the leaves directly, otherwise it is generally obtainable in liquid, ointment or gel form. Care should always be taken with any creams and mixtures from plant or other sources that they have had other additions, the original is best. Aloe vera also can be fed or used externally. I tried the latter on a badly ulcerated wound I had in a buck goat that I bought with severe footrot, the feet were easy enough to deal with, but the ulcer, near the hock, was of a long-standing and very obstinate nature. After trying anything and everything without success, the aloe vera effected healing in three days.

Apple Cider Vinegar

This simple and easily obtainable liquid is invaluable in any country where potassium is so often in short supply (this can be caused by poor farming practices). It contains natural potassium in a safe form and these days is generally available in bulk and unpasteurized from fodder stores. This is the best way to use it. Feeding quantities of apples as such can lead to digestive problems in any stock, but they will tolerate cider vinegar in large amounts, and it is wholly beneficial — a quickly assimilated source of potassium, as well as other trace minerals.

When I first read one of Dr. Jarvis's many books on cider vinegar I did as he instructed and left a container for the animals to help themselves. It may have worked in Maine where the deficiencies were not so great, but I could not afford to continue it ad lib in Australia.

Cider vinegar helps maintain the correct pH in the body, which is probably one of the reasons it is so useful. Due to its potassium content, it is invaluable for all animals just before breeding because potassium deficiencies cause blood vessel constriction, affecting the extremities and also it seems the cervix and uterus in the final stages of pregnancy; dystokia is the result. I first used cider vinegar on my milking goat herd after a season of very difficult births. The next year I was amazed at the difference, even the largest kids from maiden does arrived relatively easily and in good health. Many stock owners and human mothers have observed similar effects.

Cider vinegar given regularly to stud males will help prevent urinary calculi (water belly), and is especially useful if your rams are limited to very hard bore water as can be the case on many properties, not just in Australia. Cider vinegar added to feed twice a week would be sufficient to stop stones in the ureter or kidneys and prevention is certainly better than cure for this dangerous condition (this of course presumes that the calcium/magnesium levels are correct). A dessert spoon twice a week would be enough for sheep.

It can also be used as a mild cure for skin conditions like ring-worm when it is too close to the eyes to use a copper wash; rubbing it in well two or three times a day for a couple of days is usually enough.

Study the section on potassium for the link between sodium and potassium.

Those wishing to learn more about cider vinegar should read any of Dr. Jarvis' very interesting little books on the subject. There are various editions obtainable.

Arnica Montana

This is a perennial herb that grows in the mountains of Europe and is now being cultivated successfully in Australia; the key here was to make sure the field had balanced soil mineral-wise. It is best used in homeopathic tinctures and pillules, and ointment is available in health shops. In homeopathic form it is an excellent painkiller. I have used it post-operatively with astonishing results by normal rules. The dog (and later a cat) concerned had no idea they'd had an operation, and did not try to scratch or lick the site at all; it seems to have a healing effect as well. The dog in question has no scar from an operation to remove a salivary gland that had about 14 stitches and drainage tubes. Like vitamin C, arnica is good for shock or trauma. Another case involved an unconscious dog whose owner, trying to stop a fight hit it with a heavy stick, it recovered within three minutes of placing the arnica under its tongue. A book on veterinary homeopathy recommends that it is the first mode of treatment in *all* cases, as it calms the patients completely. It should be included in the medicine chest at all times.

It is available from homeopathic doctors, and hopefully vets. The 200C potency is most often used for sheep and other animals.

Comfrey

The old folk name for comfrey was knit-bone because it helped heal broken bones. It is a broad-leafed plant that grows quite readily in the damper, cooler areas world-wide. It will not thrive without plenty of water and a minerally balanced soil. Unfortunately comfrey tends to die back in the winter, but can sometimes be kept going in a sheltered frame where it is protect-ed from frosts. In spite of much publicity to the contrary, it is completely safe, both internally and externally. In many parts of Germany and also Japan, comfrey is used exclusively for dairy cattle fodder during the summer months. It is highly nutritious as well as being of great assistance when used internally or topically for bone problems, including breaks.

It is one of the few plants that contains natural vitamin B12, which may be one of the reasons why it is so good in the case of sickness. Comfrey may be used in poultices and will often reduce bony swellings in a matter of days. It may be made into an ointment or used as a liquid obtained by boiling the leaves; distilled comfrey oil is the best if obtainable. All forms are useful at some time or other. The plant also has the reputation as an inhibitor of cancer.

In dry weather, comfrey leaves can be offered to sheep once or twice a week, especially those that are stall fed. Animals appear to find comfrey very palatable.

Emu Oil

This is now readily obtainable from both chemists and fodder stores, as well as breeders. It is one of the by-products of emu farming. The oil should be odorless, with *no* additives; it is quickly absorbed through the skin, and is very helpful in cases of deep-seated bone injury. This was first discovered by the aboriginals of Australia, and personally I have found it invaluable; any trauma involving bruising clears up in hours, not days. It could be most valuable at shearing time.

Garlic

This is an onion-like plant that will grow prolifically if kept damp and well fed. Either the bulbs or the chopped leaves may be given. It is also available in oil-filled capsules or tablet form. Nowadays chopped garlic by the bag is available at most good fodder stores, and would certainly be beneficial for stall-fed sheep. Be careful about feeding it to milk producers as it may taint the milk.

Garlic, like onions, contains natural sulfur, and sometimes reduces the incidence of exterior parasites; it is a natural antibiotic, especially useful in intestinal disturbances. Garlic also has the reputation of being a vermifuge, and although it undoubtedly helps, in my experience it cannot entirely take the place of a balanced diet with the correct amounts of copper.

Hydrogen Peroxide (H_2O_2)

My earliest memory of this substance is fairly painful; I was a gangling child who was always making hard contact with the ground — invariably the wound was tidied up and peroxide poured on. It hurt but there was *never* any putrefaction.

There have been some astonishing results with peroxide in the livestock world. The most intransigent infections known, such as *Klebsiella* in udders (which up until recently only yields to the gun), are totally recovered in hours. A dairy farmer in the United Kingdom bought a particularly valuably British Holstein cow only to discover that her whole udder, much enlarged, was and obviously had been full of the organism for a long time. I explained how to use 6 percent peroxide (higher amounts mean a little arithmetic); in that case I said a teaspoon per quarter in two tablespoons of rainwater used as an intra-mammary. I was just leaving the country and he rang as I got home to say the animal was totally clear in four days. I had an equally satisfactory result with a goat who had been bitten in the udder by snake. Nothing else has ever worked for that and the udder eventually sloughs away. The above mixture, suitably reduced, worked in two days. In both cases, by the next lactation, the udder had freshened up normally.

Another case involved a cow with a uterine tumor; the vet offered to put her down, but the owner wanted to try peroxide. She gave a teaspoon in a pint of water by douche two or three times a day, and in two weeks there was no tumor left — much to the astonishment of her vet.

Parsley

This is one I learnt from Juliette de Baïracli-Levy's books. An old doe (goat, but it could just as easily have been a sheep) kidding late had an enormous and apparently unmilkable udder, which was causing her much distress. She was off her food. After consulting the book I found I should give her parsley. Luckily I had just one enormous parsley plant; I picked the lot, put it in a bucket, offered it to the other milkers who were not interested and then gave it to the doe. When I came out to milk an hour or two later she was standing up asking where *her* tea was. To my amazement she had eaten all the parsley, her udder had softened and I milked it out normally. The trouble did not recur. It was partly caused in her case by me being silly enough to believe the people who told me never to milk out any animal before it kidded (or lambed).

Rose Petals

These are a very old specific remedy for diarrhea, which I read about somewhere. The memory came back to me when traveling a young buck goat to its new home about 100 miles away when, at the first stop near a friend's place, I found it with bad diarrhea. Their garden was full of (unsprayed) roses and I picked about half a gallon of the flowers. The kid was nearly better before I resumed the journey, and completely clean when we pulled in at our final stop.

Drugs: What One Should Know

One of the advantages of using vitamin C (see above) is that it has no serious side effects. Any student of medicine will know that all drugs have their disadvantages, the question is whether the good the drug does outweighs its ill effects. Vitamin C, at the time of writing, is the only virucide known. Dr. Bellfield, DVM, in California uses a 200-gram dose to cure viral hepatitis in dogs. Following is a list of commonly used conventional drugs and their effects. These should seldom be used, and only as a last resort when all else has failed. Properly maintained pastures, well-grown feed, licks, and overall good care are, as always, the best prevention.

Antibiotics

These drugs have undoubtedly saved many lives in the animal and human populations; however, the fact is that continued use has made one antibiotic after another ineffective, and we have now reached the stage where very few antibiotics will work. This is why indiscriminate use of these substances is most dangerous. Organisms have built up resistance and the University of Melbourne vets told me that if any drug is suggested, insist on sensitivity tests to see if it can kill the organism — if not, do not use it. Until such time as a drug is tested as working for the relevant organism, use large injections of vitamin C, which may (as Hungerford says in his *Diseases of Livestock*) bring about a cure, but will do no harm if it does not.

It was in a sub-clinical mastitis outbreak that I had learned the chilling fact mentioned above. I had been advised to shoot about half my herd as they had previously had all the available antibiotics (I bought some of these animals when they were quite old); the next half had received almost every antibiotic, and there was one left that could be used with some hope of success — penicillin. This could have been given to the younger ones as they had never had any drugs before. I declined and started to look for safer and more effective methods of cure and prevention and, using dolomite as a carrier for the necessary calcium and magnesium, I found just that. I learned that by raising the health of the animals and the land and making sure that the herd received the necessary dolomite in their feed, mastitis and other diseases could not become a factor. Exactly the same applies to milking sheep and of course lactating wool sheep.

A few years later when the vets from the University of Melbourne were still tending my dairy goat herd, goats in Victoria were found with mycoplasma pneumonia similar to the dreaded pleuropneumonia which decimated the cattle population of Australia ("pleuro" as it was known) in the late 1800s. The vets used the only drug that they thought had a hope of working. It was given as a preventative to the whole herd when one of my goats was found sniffing and coughing, and was of the tetracycline family. They used the amount that would have been safe for a sheep, an animal very similar to a goat in size and weight. No one knew that goats could only tolerate a fraction of that amount. The result was a disaster, to the vets' horror as much as mine. It took the pregnant goats three months to die and the milkers five months, as they did not have the same strain on their systems. They all died of acute anemia, accompanied by bone marrow damage and renal failure. All efforts to save them were in vain. However, I have wondered many times since if I had used the armory of minerals and vitamins that I am now comfortable with whether I could have reversed those awful effects. Note: Erythromycin in the correct dosage can work for mycoplasma pneumonia as nothing else seems to, although I am told now that it is increasingly ineffective. It was not used on my goats.

I was constantly hoping that a safe alternative would be found to antibiotics, and eventually learned about vitamin C and its curative powers. Now we are a great deal further down the track, and veterinary experience with many different kinds of animals has increased. Make sure that a vet gives any drug that your stock may need, and *never* borrow something from another farmer or friend. If there is time, have a sensitivity test done to make sure that the drug *can* work on your particular problem. Vets tell me that when they give vitamin C with drugs, quite often the good effects are enhanced and the bad ones minimized. Bear in mind the information on vitamin B12 (above), and always insist that an injection of this vitamin is given with any antibiotic if one has to be used (two to three ml for full-grown sheep, perhaps four for a heavy ram). The senior teaching vet at the University demonstrated this to me years ago with a mare that had been very ill (colitis X); the vitamin B12 undoubtedly helped her to regain her appetite and recover. Antibiotics affect the villi in the intestines, making them shrivel up and causing aching guts in the process.

One of the reasons why we have virtually run out of effective antibiotics is the frequency with which they have been used. They are used in many cases where good nutrition and nursing would have been successful but animals were given powerful drugs because the owners did not feel like doing the work involved in better care. We took the easy option — little realizing that new drugs cannot be found indefinitely, and one cannot entirely blame the medical (veterinary and human) profession for this because people wanted a quick fix. Most "new" drugs nowadays are a cocktail of the old and tried ones.

Butazolidin (BTZ, Bute)

This is an anti-inflammatory drug and would not be given to farm stock in normal circumstances, but is quite often used on performance animals. However, I have a printout from a veterinary clinic in Victoria sent to me by a client (of mine and theirs) on my desk as I write stating that residues of this drug, or its derivatives, had been found in beef (it could have been lamb) exported to the United States. Because of this there is a possibility that they may be banned, and the clinics are advising that these substances should not be used any more. Four years later, there does not seem to be any lessening of their use.

Anti-inflammatories are painkillers, they are sometimes used in arthritic conditions and there may be a belief that they promote growth as well, which is perhaps how they were found in meat. Now that arnica for pain and boron for arthritis (see Chapter 10) are coming into widespread use, there are safe substitutes.

Remember that bute and many other anti-inflammatories have one very dangerous side effect — they weaken blood vessels, often to the point where internal hemorrhaging will cause death. The best course of action is to cure the cause of the pain, not mask it with bute or anything else. If this drug still *must* be given (and I doubt it has to), make absolutely sure that some vitamin C is given at the same time. This strengthens blood vessels, and so may avert a disaster. Arnica is really better because it helps healing as well as dulling pain, find a good homeopath — 200C is the usual strength used for animals.

One of my client's horses, appallingly lacerated after running into heavy motor traffic, is now being turned out with her incredible lesions and hematomas cleared up (four weeks later). We did not dare use bute as the blood vessels were smashed, so the trainer used arnica right through the bad initial fortnight with most satisfactory results.

Cortisone

In the section on vitamin B5 (above), I explained the mechanism for making cortisone naturally in the body. In humans, cortisone given artificially inhibits the output of natural cortisone for up to two years. I do not think anyone has found out what it does to animals, but I imagine it would be similar. So in any condition where cortisone would be indicated, such as infections, give extra vitamin C. Stock on a healthy diet with good magnesium levels should have plenty of vitamin B in the body. A lack of magnesium means low B vitamin levels (except for B12). Read the section on B5 and note that it is a component of barley (do not over-feed it); therefore that grain, with vitamin C, is needed for cortisone production in the adrenals.

Hormones

Any forms of hormones or steroids are best avoided if possible, as the after effects can be rather traumatic. My first experience put me off. A fox terrier bitch belonging to my parents was covered by the wrong dog, and the vet (in the United Kingdom) said there would be no problem, he would give her a hormone injection (stilbestrol in that instance) to make her abort. The bitch was dead of cancer of the uterus within five months. I know that drugs and methods of administration have improved over the years, but I still have not seen or heard anything that makes me think that one does not pay for the use of such substances, the body is not geared to manage the often-unknown side effects.

If steroids have to be used, remember that they have the effect of stopping the absorption of calcium and magnesium, they also either stop the synthesis of vitamin A or render it unobtainable, so the intake of that vitamin would have to be increased also. I found this out in large animals that had been given hormones for ovum transplant programs — they seemed to have persistent vitamin A and calcium/magnesium deficiency troubles for the next two years. Often the deficiency was so great after hormone administration that they could not hold to service and breed normally for that period without considerable amounts of extra cod-liver oil (vitamins A and D).

Shortage of vitamin A (and low copper levels) are the biggest causes of poor breeding performance. Goats that have been dried off with stilbestrol show the same symptoms. It took a whole lactation before their production returned to normal. After all, stilbestrol is a male hormone which would be contraindicated in a milking animal. Drying off milkers with stilbestrol is also counter productive because it acts too quickly and generally causes mastitis. The old-fashioned method of making vinegar poultices is still an effective way of drying up a milking animal if there is a good reason for doing so. A bitch whose puppies had been killed at five days was safely dry in 36 hours using that method.

However in some breeding programs there are cases where hormones have to be used, especially when introducing new breeds of livestock. Ovum transplants could not be performed if we did not have hormones; in those cases, regular supplementation with cod-liver oil must be an ongoing part of the program, which should of course include the normal minerals as found in the lick as well — otherwise there will be abortions and the whole process will be wasted.

Anthelmintics and Exterior Parasite Preventatives

Thanks to the work of Dr. William A. Albrecht, we know that interior parasites (and exterior parasites such as ticks) are caused by unhealthy land. This means that the dung beetles will not be working and copper will be low and probably sulfur also will be either missing or low in the soil. Worms do not stay in the systems of a sheep whose copper reserves are correct. Nowadays, when our soils are nowhere near what they should be (and possibly will not be so in the foreseeable future), copper sulfate and sulfur (with dolomite and seaweed meal) should be made available in licks to counteract these problems (see Chapters 4 and 8). When I worked on the land in the United Kingdom in the 1950s, worming animals just didn't figure. All animals have a few worms, and sheep farmers who have the licks out find that a count of between 100 and 200 is insignificant if the animals are on the lick. I feel that it is not the worms that are the culprit, but the lack of top-class, healthy feed.

All anthelmintics contain a poison, or they would not work. Because they are not made (these days) from natural substances, resistance to them has to become a fact of life. In France, chenopodium oil (American wormseed oil) has been routinely used for sheep as a safe, natural wormer for many years. I tried to have it imported but the chemist trying to get it in for me was knocked back once its purpose was known.

I was doing a talk for the local Department of Agriculture a few years ago, and the convener said as he introduced me: "I hope you have some answers to worms, because the drenches are becoming redundant faster than replacements can be made." Fortunately we do, and it is basically called good management. Another aspect is that organic certification cannot include the use of these substances, or those that destroy exterior parasites — equally easy to prevent. One of the facts that spelled out the demise of several drenches was their toxic after effects. Manure from drenched animals was not processed in the normal fashion by worms and dung beetles, and some other brands caused the deaths of chickens who scratched around the farmyard. In recent times some have actually caused the deaths of the animals to which they were given and in one case the vet rather apologetically told the owner that it happened occasionally. It would be interesting to know whether these animals die from anaphylaxis, or if the drench is cumulative or just unstable in its effects.

Exterior parasites only attack animals whose sulfur levels are inadequate, or animals that have sugar (from molasses) in their blood. Unfortunately, much of our land these days is sulfur deficient, and Neal Kinsey has said this many times. I had hardly ever seen lousy animals until I came to Australia in 1959, but in 1996 when visiting the United Kingdom, I found that nearly all dairy cows now have lice. Sulfur is inhibited by artificial fertilizers and these were not in general use when we left the United Kingdom in 1959, but now ammonium nitrate and superphosphate are used regularly, and I was told that most conventionally farmed dairy cows are lousy. Also the first independent soil analysis firm in Australia did not monitor sulfur, so most of us knew little if anything about it. As long as it is included in the diet in some manner, sheep should remain free of lice. Check the section on sulfur in Chapter 8 to see how incredibly important this element is, not just for lice prevention, but for the amino acids in the gut as well.

Vaccinations

Whether one agrees with these or not, there are certain facts that must be remembered when they are used. At a conference in Queensland in May 1996, Drs. Uzal and Kelly, speaking on enterotoxemia in animals, stated that the vaccinations were only effective against systemic entero and never against sudden attacks, a fact I have known for many years, but it was good to hear it aired. Systemic enterotoxemia (pulpy kidney) means that the whole herd would be sick; the nutritional status of a flock of sheep would have to be extremely low to have systemic entero.

It also a fact that any form of vaccination has the effect of depleting the vitamin C almost wholly in the body. Normally this would not be a problem, but it was in the case of a horse my neighbor brought up to Maldon in the heat (around 112 degrees) of the summer from a totally bare paddock down south. It had not been floated for several years and was not supplemented at all and was probably slightly stressed as a consequence. The vendor followed it into the float and gave it its vaccines — tetanus and strangles I believe. The next day I noticed it looking extremely unwell and went over to inquire if anyone had seen any snakes around. They had, so I rushed home for a vitamin C injection, by the time I got back the horse was swaying and going down by the back legs. I gave it the injection, and within two minutes it was all right — too quick for snakebite and its eyes were normal; previously they had been partially closed and it was impossible to see if the pupils were dilated or not. I was wondering what on earth had been the problem when the owner said it could not be ill because it had been vaccinated as it was leaving its former home. Obviously its vitamin C intake in recent months must have been incredibly low — a horse on a healthy paddock makes 30-plus grams a day in its liver, a sheep, 15-plus grams. If vaccinations are necessary, see that the vitamin C levels are raised accordingly in any animal if conditions are bad. The above story could so easily have happened to any other stock.

Chapter 10

Health Problems

Statistics

Temperature:	101 F
Respiration:	10-20 breaths per minute
Pulse:	70-90 per minute
Gestation:	155 days
Cycle:	17 days
Cycle length:	36 hours
Ovulates:	from 24th to 36th hour

Most health problems are the result of faulty or inadequate nutrition. These problems will often respond to replacing the missing minerals or vitamins, the absence of which cause the so-called disease. In other words, pathogens like a medium, or host, that is deficient in certain essential minerals. Mastitis, which is a very uneconomic condition in sheep, whatever their purpose, only strikes animals whose calcium/magnesium levels are out of balance; a lack of copper in the diet can also contribute. Gut illnesses are often due to an altered pH in the sheep due to poor pasture, hay or feed. A prominent judge told me years ago that he, like most people, believed that the ratio was 50 percent heredity and 50 percent management; now he has changed that to 10 percent heredity and 90 percent management. It does not matter how well bred the sheep is; if the feed does not match up, all the breeding is wasted.

Below I have listed the conditions by their best known names and put their other names in parentheses.

Abscess (Cheesy Gland, Grass Seed Abscess, *Caseous Lymphadenitis* or CLA)

Strictly speaking, all these are not caused by the same thing, but where there is an infective agent the causative germ is usually corynebacteria. It is virtually impossible to stop one of these abscesses coming up. Drugs do not help. The university used my goats as guinea pigs when an outbreak of CLA (vaccination needle induced) broke out. Every stage and every usable drug was tried. We never stopped any of them. If the abscess is lanced before it is "ripe," it will usually result in such a mess so that the operator will remember never to do it again. The best way is to catch the boil just as it is ready to burst. Wear rubber gloves and squeeze out the pus, burning everything used afterwards. Once the abscess is clear, syringe it out well with a one-third mixture of copper sulphate to water to which a tablespoon of vinegar has been added — hydrogen peroxide is also excellent, as explained in Chapter 9. Comfrey ointment will help healing.

An injection of three to four grams of vitamin C for a sheep may be given when the abscess is forming — sometimes it will speed it up. In cases where the abscess is on the side of the throat, and is very big, occasionally it goes right through to the gullet. When this happens, much of the poison goes into the system. Injections and oral doses of vitamin C as above should be given for several days to stop the risk of further infection.

Caseous lymphadenitis is the name given to a condition where the boils become endemic. They do not limit themselves to the first one, which is often caused by a grass seed, but continue down the line of the lymph system. If the sheep is really healthy, its immune system can sort it out, but if the immune system is weak, the boils may end up forming inside with often fatal results. Sometimes a week of 15 to 20 ml of vitamin C daily by injection will bring them through — it has been done.

Much of the above is academic with sheep since often the abscesses are not seen at all if the fleece is halfway to maturity or more. An abscess definitely can occur from contact through a break in the skin, occasionally from a grass seed, but far more likely from a shearing cut or as the result of mulesing.

Abscess was a big problem in Angora goats in South Africa, which were shorn and marked in yards made out in the bush as often happens in Australia for these operations on sheep. It was realized that the corynebacteria lived in the soils and the goats were reinfected each time they came in contact with the soil. The cycle was broken almost completely by moving the yards to fresh ground each year, as mentioned previously. Vaccinations did not make much difference, but good management did.

Note: CLA has been classified in the United Kingdom as a zoonose, which means it can be caught by humans (as can most animal diseases).

Anemia (Iron or Cobalt Deficiency)

This is a huge problem in Australia, although it should not be as bad in the United States because the soils there are better. Signs of anemia are ill thrift, wasting and very pale membranes, particularly on the inside of the bottom eyelid. Examining this membrane occasionally will enable the farmer to have a reasonable idea of the health of the flock. Blood-sucking worms like Barber's Pole Worm *(Haemonchus contortus)* and Brown Stomach Worm *(Ostertagia)* can be the cause. Lack of iron and/or cobalt and copper can be another. In Australia anemia is not generally caused by a lack of iron, there is usually too much of it, but iron cannot be utilized without copper and a lack of that mineral is generally the cause of iron anemia.

The reason for the anemia must be dealt with; worms must be killed, and the red blood count built up once more. Giving seaweed and fish products will help build up iron. Injections of Vitamin B12 should also be given to help the cobalt levels, and the copper content of the diet must be attended to, usually by the lick already mentioned. Remineralize the pasture to a state where the copper is available again. Copper is inhibited by very low (or very high) pH, but can be top-dressed in the latter case.

Iron tonics should be used as little as possible because they depress vitamin E. As above, vitamin B12 injections daily for a week will be a great help (one ml of each for a small lamb and two of each for a sheep). This can be put in the same syringe with a little vitamin C (see appendix for information on VAM).

If the anemia is due to a lack of cobalt, in which case the membranes may be quite a good color, injected B12 and possibly cobalt supplementation will be needed. Signs of cobalt anemia are subnormal temperature and cold extremities. Scouring eventually ensues, as will death, if something is not done. Unbalanced pH levels can inhibit cobalt as can artificial fertilizers, find out the cause and remineralize where necessary so that the land is as good as it can be. In districts like some in South Australia and in West Australia the addition of *two* pounds of cobalt sulfate to the lick mentioned has been found to be effective. Start with half that and if problems still occur raise it slightly.

Anthrax (Cumberland Disease, Loodana Fever, Charbon or Horse Plague)

This disease seems to occur in high, humid temperatures on land where the pH is very low. It was first reported in Australia in 1847, according to Hungerford. It can and does live in the soil for many years in those conditions. Due to lack of knowledge in the past, afflicted animals have often been consigned to the nearest swamp instead of burning the carcases where they lie, as is emphasized by the veterinary profession. Sheep and cattle are particularly vulnerable, and vaccination only works if it has been implemented *before* the animal is infected — as with all such treatments, it is unsuccessful once the organism is in action. (Note: this vaccination cannot be given to horses at *any* time, as it can cause the disease). When an animal dies of anthrax the spores proliferate, so immediate burning or burial, moving the corpse as little as possible, are the safest options and should be accompanied by the use of disinfectants.

In a flock of sheep dead animals are often the first sign, otherwise a very high temperature (above 104 degrees) followed by convulsions and death have been reported. Blood-stained urine has also been reported by Hungerford in an outbreak that he attended.

Flies can spread the disease by blood transfer between individuals and species — it is a zoonose – and the greatest attention to hygiene and cleanliness is necessary. Anthrax can be fatal in humans; call a vet *immediately* if it is suspected and prepare to burn the carcass — do *not* move it.

Arthritis

Systemic arthritis is caused by poor absorption or lack of calcium, magnesium, copper and boron. Low levels of the latter in the soil are probably the biggest cause; any level below .4 ppm would merit attention. Study the oldest sheep in the flock, they will show arthritis first.

On farms where the analysis shows low levels of boron to be the case, three tablespoons of borax can be added to the standard lick. Seaweed meal occasionally provides enough of the mineral to stop arthritis if the boron is between .4 and .6 ppm. Ideally, it should be about .8 to 1.0 ppm on most analyses. For affected sheep, take all the grain out of the diet, give good hay from a remineralized paddock and give the lick as above. If sheep are confined, give four grams per head with a gram of borax daily for five days or until the arthritis is relieved. Five ml of cod-liver oil should be given once a week. The sheep should improve in ten days. A maintenance dose of boron will be needed thereafter.

Cider vinegar added to the diet also helps, and if hand fed, the sheep should be confined to good grass hay, chaff and bran with the above additives and *no* grain. Attend to the land and make sure artificials are not used.

Infective Arthritis (Polyarthritis)

This is always the result of an organism, usually corynebacteria (again), entering the body through a shearing cut, the navel cord, mulesing or marking; occasionally it can be spread venereally if a ram becomes infected. However, the majority of the cases reported in sheep appear to be the result of mulesing, as it seems the general practice is to drop the lamb onto the dirty ground tail-first once the operation has been completed. I have suggested that a bed of wool soaked in disinfectant could be used, but better still, put the lambs down on their feet so the raw tail does not come in contact with the ground, which is always liable to carry infections in yards. (This has been covered in the management section also.)

Infective (poly) arthritis is almost impossible to treat because the bacteria is highly resistant to drugs. Also, by the time the joints become hot and swollen, the organism has already caused a great deal of irreversible damage, and the sheep will never be fully sound again, even if the bacteria can be controlled. Bearing this in mind, as treatment is rarely successful with conventional drugs, large doses of vitamin C, 15 ml (7.5 grams) and above per day, both intravenous and by mouth, have been tried with this ailment and have sometimes killed the organism. Supportive measures such as B12 injections should also be given.

This method has been used with horses successfully.

Blackleg

This is a clostridial disease, and is caused by *Clostridium feseri (chauvoei), bacillus chauvoei* and *B. anthracis symptomatis*. It is possible that, like other clostridial diseases, any of these may inhabit a normal gut without causing trouble, *but* if the diet becomes unbalanced, they will start to proliferate.

The other usual mode of entry is via a wound — usually rather small — that either has not been seen or not deemed worth disinfecting. Blackleg is reckoned to be incurable; however, several cases have been pulled through successfully. Blackleg should be controlled by annual immunizations, but apparently this does not always happen.

The first lesson the vets I worked with in the United Kingdom hammered home was that a wound must be properly disinfected only *once*, as disinfecting inhibited healing. They used peroxide, iodine, disinfectant (Lysol in those days) and, if all else failed alcohol — gin, whisky or whatever. A 10 percent copper sulfate solution is also very effective. If necessary, this disinfectant must be syringed hard into the wound and all dirt removed if possible. Unfortunately, both with this disease and tetanus, the wound is often too small to be noticed.

When using vitamin C by injection for any illness, it generally stings temporarily. When an animal is really ill they do not react to it, but as they get better they start to show signs of pain, which is when you change to oral administration. However, with blackleg the body appears to be so sensitized that they show acute pain from the injection done in the normal place, such as the neck, or anywhere else. I treated the last animal I cured of this ailment the usual way, with the neck injections, and realized I was getting nowhere. Then I tried the treatment described below.

In Blackleg the limb, usually a rear one, swells to grotesque proportions. The beast is in great pain. It can only lie on the ground with the affected limb pointing skyward. In a goat or sheep the diameter of the leg can easily be between one to two feet across.

Inject straight into the swollen limb repeatedly (every few hours) with 50 ml of vitamin C. Usually two injections reduce the swelling so that the leg can rest and be bent. Give good supportive nursing and an injection of B12 in the neck — you may use a 21-gauge needle for the latter. The vitamin C injection needs an 18-gauge needle. As soon as the patient is eating again give sodium ascorbate powder in the feed. Continue to inject the affected limb with vitamin C until the swelling goes down completely (about 24 hours). Find and disinfect the cause if possible. This would be worth doing with a valuable animal and, of course, sensible follow-up treatment is necessary. The sheep cannot just be tipped out to take its chances once the leg is normalized, it must be kept under observation for a few days.

Bloat

Bloat is sign of a sick farm, the cause being potassium and magnesium that are deficient or greatly out of balance. If the land has been farmed organically and remineralized, bloat will not occur. The stands of solid clover that occur in unbalanced fields, and that often cause bloat, do not grow where the soil has been properly balanced; a ratio no higher than 50 percent clover to the rest of the pasture is as much as is needed on any farm, and less clover will do.

For a sheep with mild bloat, about two pints of cooking oil (not liquid paraffin, soy or canola) will help lubricate the insides so some of the wind can be dissipated from one end or the other. The drench should be followed by enforced exercise. I found with sheep that pushing them along and massaging their sides at the same time often worked wonders. Also giving a drench of cider vinegar and honey with dolomite will help redress the magnesium to potassium imbalance.

However, if the bloat is acute and the animal is down, it will be necessary to release the gas. If this is not done, the pressure will build up to the point where the sheep suffocates and/or the organs cannot function. The gas has to be released with a pointed knife or a trokar, a sharp, hollow instrument that allows the gas to escape. The gut should be pierced on the left side about a hand's width behind the last rib, halfway down the abdomen. If using a sharp knife, insert it and twist slightly — the gas will come out very quickly. Put the knife or whatever in only as far as is needed to release the pressure. Be sure to disinfect the opening before and afterwards. A drench of liquid kelp and cider vinegar will help the animal recover. An injection of vitamin C would also be a good safeguard —10 ml for a sheep.

Bloat in Hand-Fed Lambs

This is a different scenario, especially if the lamb has been fed artificial milk replacer (raw sheep's or goat's milk are perfectly safe). Many of the milk replacers contain tallow butylhydroxide or similar ingredients and this-high fat substance (for some reason manufacturers put 18 percent fat in many of these replacers in spite of the fact that neither sheep's, goat's or cow's milk ever reach those butterfat levels) coats the inside of the intestines so that the lamb cannot absorb any nutrients. The first sign is bloat, and the normal cures do not work, as I found when trying to save the life of a goat thus fed years ago. It had to be destroyed. Always check a milk replacer extremely carefully and use the ordinary full-cream, powdered milk from the store if sheep's or goat's milk are not obtainable.

Blood in the Milk

This is usually caused by a blood vessel breaking in the udder, often at the start of a lactation due to the ewe's milk coming down very fast. It can also be caused by a blow, in which case there may be a mark, or it may be the precursor to mastitis. Ease off on the grain and give the sheep a dessert spoon of vitamin C in the feed for a couple of days as this usually clears it up very quickly. Vitamin C strengthens blood vessels and helps in recovery from injuries.

Bovine Spongiform Encephalitis (BSE) and Allied Diseases

The jury is still out on this one it seems. That said, every stock owner needs to know the nuts and bolts of transmission. This is drawn from Mark Purdey's information and his thesis in *Harcourt Medical Publishers 2000*, much of which had already appeared in *Acres U.S.A.*

I first read of this affliction in 1984, when I was sent Stanley Prusiner's thesis "Prions" from the *Scientific American*, October 1984. There were many pages and it seemed at the time a possible answer to BSE and all its variants in other species, including humans. Prusiner considered prions to be a small "germ" without DNA or RNA, which reached the system of the cattle involved by way of meat meal processed by the low-heat method as this was cheaper than the high-heat process that preceded it. This method came into use about the late '70s.

Prusiner did not know, and apparently no one else did either, or they kept quiet, that prions are a normal part of all brains. It has been suggested that their possible role is as a preventative against Alzheimer's and afflictions similar to BSE. It has also been established (see below) that as long as the host's brain has adequate copper, the prions stay healthy.

Those who have read this book thus far will know just how easy it is to fall below the adequate copper state. This very necessary mineral is lost when phosphatic fertilizers, or other substances involving high phosphates or artificial nitrogen (as in urea, ammonium nitrate, etc.) are used. André Voisin postulates there is 100 percent loss of available copper where they are used, and we cannot afford that. Also the minerals molybdenum and manganese suppress copper, as does zinc when its levels are too high and out of balance. "Moly's" role in this suppression has been common knowledge for many years. Zinc and copper were each thought to depress the other, according to which was highest, but this was disproved. Copper never suppressed zinc, but, as above, the reverse can happen. I did not know that manganese also has a cupro-suppressive effect, until I received the research listed below.

Prusiner's 1984 thesis apparently became common knowledge in the United Kingdom about ten years later. The dairy farmers I knew in the United Kingdom were told about it in 1994 and around that time the meat meal used by conventional farmers was banned. In Australia that happened in May 1996.

Meat meal was replaced by processed chicken litter from battery chickens in egg-producing factories. Apparently chickens in these circumstances receive high quantities of manganese in their feed in order to make them lay — that also was new knowledge to me. Our commercial free-range layers in the post war years in the United Kingdom managed very well without it.

The theory is that BSE comes back to the use of organophosphate "back liners," which are used to deter parasites. It was mandatory for these to be used triple strength. The chemicals involved were organophosphates such as Phosmet. Purdey refused to use them as he farmed organically and uses Derris dust should warble flies and their grubs become a problem. One of my jobs when working with the land army post war was to squeeze these same grubs out of cattle as the cows lay relaxed in the paddock (they are uneconomical as they ruin a good hide).

When these back lined cattle are treated with the above organophosphate, the manganese already in the body (from the chicken litter) combines with it before it reaches the brain. This chelates the copper in the healthy prions, they fold over and the prions go rogue for want of a better term, and the trail to brain degeneration is set.

A graph by Mark Purdey listing the first use of these materials in the rural parts of France is most chilling: 88 districts are listed. Then the dates on which the chemicals were first administered are shown, starting in 1986, and the first emergence of BSE for that district was five years later. This started at all localities approximately four to five years after the chemicals were used, but seemed to speed up by the year 2000. Thus Allier, France, where the chemical was used in 1998, shows BSE by the year 2,000.

Purdey has also done extensive work around industries and localities where manganese is heavily used. The history of areas where manganese was used in industrial processes in the early part of the 20th century reports "manganese madness" among the unfortunate workers.

It comes back to the undoubted fact that if we learn to farm naturally without chemicals and cease to feed animal wastes, from whatever source, back to cattle and other stock, these terrible afflictions will not arise. Factory farming of any kind produces intransigent waste products. Cattle and all other stock can be produced without this; nowadays feed lot time is being reduced; customers are expressing a preference for grass fed meat, which really does taste good. We do not have any other option for animal and human health.

Cancer

This condition is rare in sheep, but when it does occur it is nearly always due to a diet too high in phosphate-rich food from paddocks that have been top-dressed with superphosphate and/or nitrogen in some form. Therefore they lack magnesium, calcium, potassium and copper. According to André Voisin, the latter is always missing in cancer cases. Lack of iodine and vitamin A can also be causative factors.

If the animal is very valuable, megadoses of vitamin C accompanied by extra vitamin A will help. Use 70,000 units of vitamin A (fish oil derived) and at least 15 grams of vitamin C twice daily. Put the sheep onto an organic mixed pasture, not legumes. Quite a few animals have been put into total remission by this method.

Circling Disease

This can be caused by listeriosis or in some cases by corynebacteria affecting the brain, making the sheep one sided to the point where it can only move in circles. The gait is usually slightly stiff, with the head stuck forward. In a post mortem these two culprits can be confirmed by a vet.

However one of the most usual causes is a nasal bot that has crawled up into the brain and caused damage. There is unfortunately nothing that can be done, and the affected sheep should be put down. In these circumstances the meat is still quite safe to eat, but not in the case of the first two.

Coccidiosis

This is caused by a protozoa and particularly affects young sheep; older ones can become immune to it and be carriers all their lives. Signs are blood-stained droppings and ill thrift. The old remedy was a sulfa drug called sulfadimidine. This type of drug has been largely phased out now. It is fortunate that we have found copper supplied to sheep as needed (in licks) means that coccidiosis is another condition that seems to be a thing of the past. If the older carriers are on the lick and properly fed they should eventually become clear.

This is one of the diseases that people who have their sheep on the right amount of copper never encounter. I have not seen it for 25 years, but it was a serious problem in the early days. It is supposed to be species specific, but outbreaks occur in rather unlikely situations that could only be explained by possible bird contamination, so I wonder about that.

Contracted Tendons (Knuckle-Over)

This is seen in newly born lambs. The front legs are twisted or curled under, the lambs have difficulty in walking, and they look as though they are walking on their toes. A teaspoon of cod-liver oil straight in the mouth will start the cure. It may have to be given once or twice more, but recovery generally takes place in 12 hours. This condition is due to poor pastures or drought when the ewe has not had enough green stuff to provide adequate quantities of vitamins A and D. This is why a drench of cod-liver oil, ideally mixed with liquid kelp at a rate of five ml of each, should always be given to ewes once a week for the last three weeks coming up to lambing, particularly if the season has been extra dry or hard.

Cowpox

This could affect milk sheep, generally in their first lactation. It is very contagious in animals whose copper reserves are too low. It is caused by a herpes-linked organism, and, if nothing is done, is difficult to stop before it runs its cycle (three weeks). This condition only strikes when the sheep is deficient in copper and a copper/cider vinegar wash exteriorly as used for scabby mouth or ringworm helps the scabs to dry up and drop off in twenty four hours. In very deficient animals cowpox can spread over the whole body — *not* desirable in a ewe carrying a fleece — and care must be taken to see the sores do not become infected. Vitamin C injections should be given before that occurs. At least 20 ml (10 grams) twice a day at first. Make sure the patient has access to the lick.

Dermatitis (Dermo)

This affects sheep of all ages if they are deficient enough in copper. The wool, generally on the back, gives a good imitation of a nylon pot-scourer, often reaching from the base of the neck to the tail. Fly strike in that nasty mess is very bad news indeed. The diet must be adjusted to prevent dermo. The licks already mentioned should be given. If they are not available, they should be made up quickly. A teaspoon of the lick given to each sufferer daily for about a week will lift the dermatitis enough to shear the sheep and clean it up. My daughter, who is a wool classer, tried this on two badly affected sheep she managed to acquire, and the fleece grew enough to enable her husband to shear the whole horrid mess off in about eight days.

Fleece Rot

This is not often seen nowadays. Fleece Rot is caused by *Pseudomonas* bacteria and would occur only in sheep that are undernourished and/or minerally deficient. It does not occur in sheep receiving their minerals in the lick already mentioned and is almost certainly caused by a lack of copper and sulfur.

Dystokia (Difficult Birth)

The cause of dystokia is a lack of potassium, and it is too late to remedy this when you are pulling lambs out one after another. Until the farm is healthy enough for potassium to be obtainable naturally, cider vinegar, which is a great source of the mineral, has to be used. Each ewe should receive about five ml twice a week for the month preceding lambing. This is easily done by feeding hay sprayed with cider vinegar a couple of times a week. Work out the amounts so that the ewes receive the quantities suggested — more will do no harm. Liquid seaweed (that does *not* contain chelates or additives) can be added to the brew in about the same amounts and is also a great pre-lambing tonic. Always use unpasteurized bulk cider vinegar, which should be readily available at most fodder stores.

This is where a soil analysis can be invaluable. From a complete analysis, the farmer at least will know by the potassium levels if the sheep are likely to succumb to dystokia. Pulling lambs is not desirable as it is highly stressful for ewe, lamb and farmer.

Eczema

This condition is fairly rare in sheep, although pigs and alpacas can also be affected. About 30 years ago in New Zealand, outbreaks of facial eczema in sheep were found to be due to a lack of zinc in the sheep's diets, and it was soon brought under control when that mineral was fed. Zinc is naturally well supplied in seaweed products, and zinc sulfate rarely has to be used for sheep.

Enterotoxemia (Entero, Pulpy Kidney)

This ailment is caused by *Clostridium welchii* or, in rare cases, *Clostridium perfringens D*, both organisms that can normally be found in the gut of any ruminant. If the diet becomes unbalanced due to worms, too little iodine, inadequate minerals, minerally unbalanced fields or plain starvation, the bacteria starts to proliferate, and in so doing gives off a deadly toxin. Death is usually rapid.

Sheep show great distress and lose the use of their back legs; *very* quick action with vitamin C may save an animal. A dose of 20 ml (10 grams) by injection and 20 grams by mouth (a tablespoon of sodium ascorbate), repeated every few hours could work. This should be accompanied by dolomite put into the mouth (dolomite cannot be dissolved) at the same time. A dessert spoon of dolomite with a quarter teaspoon of sulfur and seaweed meal should be given at the same time as the vitamin C.

Unfortunately, the vaccinations, which are inclined to give farmers a false sense of security, cannot work if conditions and husbandry are poor. At a conference in Queensland in 1996, Drs. Uzal and Kelly (veterinarians) gave a talk on enterotoxemia and said the vaccinations only work in flocks with systemic entero, and even in systemic cases, they are not always successful.

The vaccinations do *not* stop severe cases. The vaccinations are now obtainable in various combinations, from two-in-one with tetanus through to five-in-one, etc. Normally animals have boosters each year, although it is the young who are most at risk. Ewes are generally given one dose in the month before lambing to protect the offspring until marking at six weeks of age, when the lambs will be vaccinated in their turn.

Vets are beginning to feel that the dangers of enterotoxemia are often over-rated, and that if husbandry and land management particularly are good, it is not the scourge we have been led to believe it to be. The first book I read on the subject in the early '60s said it was not an ailment that affected sheep or other animals that received all their necessary minerals and dietary requirements.

Enzootic Ataxia

According to André Voisin this is another disease that arises when copper is inadequately supplied, prevention would be easier than cure. I think that two ml of VAM, two ml B12 and 15 ml of vitamin C would be worth trying.

Flag

Flag is a condition of the udder that can occur when a sheep first comes into milk. The udder is hard, and the milk does not let down. Flag is usually worse around the sides of the quarters. Removing high-protein feed and *all* legumes — even clover should be avoided — from the diet will go a long way to helping it clear up. Feed dolomite as suggested and yellow feed, i.e., chaff, bran and grass hay. Once the condition has cleared up, the normal diet can be given. Flag occasionally runs in families. It rarely occurs on healthy pastures.

Fly Strike

This problem is definitely worse on farms where the minerals in the soil are out of balance or missing and is therefore a scourge in Australia. The use of conventional fertilizers make it worse, especially in districts where the soils are poor and pH low. The Vermont and Rambouillet breeds of sheep with their deep folds of skin were totally unviable in Australia because those deep folds provide shelter for maggots. These breeds have been a success in the United States because of the better-quality soil.

Those sheep masters who see that their flocks have licks made from dolomite, as suggested in earlier chapters, report that the incidence of fly strike has fallen considerably, even in really bad years.

One farmer in New South Wales who had sheep on new land was having a very high incidence of strike. Within a week of putting out the licks as suggested above, the damage dropped to almost nil. Quite a few sheep were struck, but the maggots bailed out immediately and did no further damage.

In the late '50s and early '60s in Victoria, fly strike was limited to wounds on daggy or scouring sheep and checking them over daily in humid weather was fairly routine. Then when the droving mobs came through from the northern states in the 1965 drought, we were faced with a new scourge, the small green blow fly that crawled in under the wool anywhere at all and laid its maggots (body strike). These flies really made sheep farming hard work in warm, humid weather. I used to ride through the mob twice a day when conditions were bad, run them into a corner and sit on the horse watching — a very good vantage point — until I saw a twitch, and that was often all one did see. I would grab the sheep and as often as not find an area the size of my hand underneath the wool just crawling with maggots. These strikes could be on any part of the body.

Often a struck sheep will lie apart from the others, and should of course be examined at once. Struck sheep should be clipped around the strike area and cleaned up. Nowadays, with the demand for organic wool on the increase, most conventional fly strike dressings cannot be used because they are so toxic. These dressings are also very hard on sheep. Neem oil, should it become available, is reputed to be a safe non-toxic dressing; however, it is not allowed as an input in some organic certifications programs.

Foot and Mouth Disease (Herpes Rhinovirus)

This is a notifiable disease, where small runny vesicles appear round the tongue, lips and between the toes of ruminants. It is spread by birds, infected feedstuffs and contact. It affects cloven-hoofed stock, including sheep.

An authenticated story from Holland told how two out of three farms on the same neck of land had foot and mouth. The cows on the middle farm, which had contact with the other two, were organically farmed and fed seaweed meal ad lib. They never did contract it. Holland, unlike England and Australia, does not have the total eradication policy, so that situation could not arise here where all cows on all three of the farms would have been destroyed.

There are other conditions that look like foot and mouth disease, but after notification (which is mandatory) they have been found to be fairly harmless. The disease has been in Australia several times since the first outbreak in 1870, and has never spread like it does in cold, wet countries.

In the latest book on vitamin C, Dr. Glen Dettman, *et al.*, in the section on animal diseases, lists foot and mouth disease as one that is curable with large doses of vitamin C. Foot and mouth did not occur on any organic farms in the United Kingdom during the 2001 outbreak, likely because they gave their sheep kelp. A paper by Dr. John Fitzherbert suggests that the virus in humans and animals is only active when zinc is missing, and this mineral is particularly high in kelp products.

Footrot (Footscald)

Due to some of the rather draconian reactions to the finding of footrot or its precursor, footscald, this condition has some very unhappy connotations these days. Every old veterinary book that I have been able to find states that it is purely a condition associated with a deficiency of copper. The initial stage of footrot, often long before anything is noticed, is redness between the sheep's toes. At this stage the keratin in the animal's system has broken down and the skin can no longer withstand the attack of the footrot germ. Hair, hooves and horns (in some species) depend on keratin for maximum health. Keratin depends on adequate copper and sulphur, and if these minerals are lacking, a breakdown as just described takes place.

The disease causes smelly, suppurating and very sore feet, sometimes with large flesh growths forming in between the toes. When this happens, a sprinkling of straight copper sulfate on the growth, after dipping the feet in the copper wash, will help the growth to disintegrate. Foot baths of 20-percent copper sulfate can be used, but the interior form of administration is the most effective. Copper sulfate is very alkaline, and adding some vinegar or detergent to the bath will make it more efficient; vinegar acts as a water softener, and the mixture soaks right into the lesions.

Sheep who have permanent access to the stock lick mentioned will not have problems with footrot or scald. Like many other foot diseases in other species, it seems that adequate copper in the diet is the answer. When one remembers that this mineral is 100 percent inhibited by phosphatic and nitrogenous fertilizers, it is not surprising that there are so many problems.

Footscald (see Footrot)

Grass Tetany

This condition arises because magnesium and calcium are too low in the pastures. The treatment is injections of magnesium and calcium, available from the vet or fodder stores. The injections should be given as soon as the first signs are seen. On farms where bore water (which often contains magnesium in high amounts) is used for drinking, the stock on the bores do not seem to succumb, while those on dam water will go down very rapidly. It does not occur on properly remineralized paddocks and/or while the licks are available.

Impaction (Constipation)

When a sheep is constipated, the manure becomes very hard, dry and difficult to pass. A drench of cooking oil will act as a lubricant, use 250 ml for a full-grown sheep. Patients look hunched up and uncomfortable and should be drafted into a yard for observation. Sometimes dried dung can be felt at a rectal examination and an enema might help. It is quite often caused in very dry conditions if the water supply is not good enough, but it is a rare condition. Vitamin C powder drenched in with water can also help. An enema of warm water, 50 ml at a time, works fairly fast, especially if accompanied by the drench above.

Infertility (Poor Lambing Percentages)

These are generally due to various mineral and vitamin deficiencies; the minerals selenium and copper and the vitamins A and D are mainly implicated. However (assuming the rams are fertile), the most usual cause of low lambing percentages is nearly always a lack of copper in the diet; this means that ewes may not come in season as they should. I am constantly amazed at the low lambing percentages that farmers seem to accept as the norm; one farmer told me that 30 percent was usual. There is really no reason for lambing percentages to be less than the high nineties; good lambing percentages are one of the improvements reported in flocks where the minerals have been properly supplemented.

Ewes that fail to hold to service (again assuming that the rams are fertile), unless non-breeders, are suffering from a lack of vitamin A. An injection or drench of vitamin A and D (or A, D and E) before the next heat will usually mean the failure will not occur again. Feeding the stock on a well-grown, and preferably organic, green crop should ensure holding to service. This sort of infertility is apt to occur after or during a long drought (which is probably how the native fauna in Australia are regulated). Particular care should be taken of the rams because a vitamin A-related infertility is usually irreversible in males. Regular cod-liver oil, about 10 ml at a time once a month for "resting" rams should be enough to keep them in good health in very dry seasons.

A lack of selenium is another reason for infertility in rams. When selenium is insufficient, the sperm will be weak and few in quantity, and those that are there will tend to drop their tails. Luckily seaweed contains selenium in organic form, and making sure that stud rams receive it regularly, with the lick containing the sulfur, will go a long way to ensuring sperm quality and quantity (see section on selenium in Chapter 8).

Another cause can be lack of libido which is associated with low pasture manganese, however again the seaweed in the lick should take care of this. Restoring the pastures after analyzing and remineralization should adjust the manganese levels. Manganese, given the work done by an English dairy farmer called Mark Purdey, on the causes of Bovine Spongiform Encephalitis and its various forms, should be kept well within the normal parameters.

Injuries

All Injuries

Sadly, in sheep injuries are often caused by attacks from predators. With any injury tetanus and blackleg must always be considered as a possibility, even when the victims have been vaccinated. Tetanus usually takes 10 days to incubate, occasionally longer; blackleg is possibly the same. Cleaning and disinfecting the wound really well helps to avoid the problem. A tetanus antitoxin injection and daily injections of vitamin C for a fortnight, or until the wound heals, should prevent tetanus. Use 10 grams of vitamin C the first day and thereafter six to seven grams for sheep. Give all injections in the muscle.

For bad wounds, the same amount of vitamin C with about 3,000 units of vitamin E given for a few days will help in healing wounds. As for tetanus, disinfect thoroughly the first time; this is a good rule of thumb with all wounds. Application of an antiseptic oil such as lavender will keep flies off the wound until it heals, unless bandaging is necessary. If the injury is in meat sheep due for slaughter, use a non-smelling oil.

Broken Bones

Sheep with broken bones can be helped as they, unlike larger animals, are not too heavy to support themselves. A broken leg can be carefully splinted, bound up, and the sheep restrained. In a reasonably young patient healing should take place in a 10-14 days.

Shear the leg and bandage it into the correct position with a firm, but not too tight, bandage. Apply the splints (use flat pieces of wood or a metal type which looks like a ladder and is obtainable from the vet, whichever works best), and secure them with a good, strong bandage. This last bandage is best sewn into place so that it cannot come undone or get caught on snags. This should be left on until the sheep goes sound and puts weight on the limb properly once more. Plaster of Paris is not really suitable for animals as it must be kept dry and is very heavy and clumsy.

In the case of a compound fracture, when the bone is sticking through the skin, thorough disinfecting of the wound is very important, followed by stitching, bandaging and splinting as before, but this is strictly a job for the vet. Unless the sheep is very valuable from a stud point of view, it is really kinder to put it down at once.

Skin Wounds

In sheep these mostly occur at shearing time, and these days it does not seem to be fashionable to use Stockholm tar on them. I am not sure why it worked so well. In Australia we use a phenol-based oil named Flints Oils, similar to one in the United Kingdom called Green Oils; both of these promote healing and keep flies well away.

Always disinfect bad cuts; there are far too many accounts of infections like polyarthritis occurring from shearing wounds nowadays. These are not always avoidable, but as long as correct care is taken they should not cause long-term damage. A teaspoon of 6-percent hydrogen peroxide in half a pint of water works well. If you use iodine, make sure it contains no additives.

Johne's Disease
(Mycobacterium paratuberculosis)

This disease is caused by a bacterium and it is another notifiable disease. The bacterium lodges in the walls of the intestines and sets up inflammation. This causes the sheep to ultimately die of starvation due to poor absorption of nutrients. This bacterium is only present in sheep who are deficient in copper. They cannot contract it — even with contact — if the land is healthy and they are on the stock lick already recommended.

Most countries insist on stock from a Johne's-free farm for their imports. Johne's is a disease, which, if the animal is valuable enough, can be cured and it is wholly preventable; the land and husbandry must be addressed immediately and the conditions that cause a lack of copper must be removed. Low pH soils inhibit the mineral and it cannot be spread at a pH lower than 5.8, otherwise it will be sulfated out due to the soil acidity (see Chapter 6 on land management).

The disease is quite curable with large doses of vitamin C and by ensuring that the sheep receives *all* its necessary minerals.

Some people believe that Johne's (and Crohn's, the human version) are due to a deficiency of copper and zinc, which is apparently responsible for a number of inflammatory diseases. Copper seems to be the most important; however, there seems little doubt that it, like many other conditions, is related to bad husbandry and/or lack of the correct minerals, particularly copper. For many years it was thought that Johne's was always contracted at birth and that it would show up at some later date. This is undoubtedly one source of infection, but it is now realized that a perfectly healthy animal, if treated badly enough, can contract it as well. The organism is probably present in the soil of far more farms than is realized. Regardless of the reason for infection, a cure is quite possible if started before the animal becomes too weak.

Signs of Johne's disease are wasting, recurring ill thrift and diarrhea. If animals present with these symptoms have the vet take a blood test. The organism causes thickening of the intestine walls to the point where the sheep can no longer obtain the nutrients it needs and it dies of starvation. At postmortem enlarged lymph nodes can be present, but, as pointed out in a paper from the University of Liverpool, enlarged lymph nodes are *not* always a sign of Johne's disease (the paper was a reprint from *Veterinary Preventative Medicine*, see bibliography).

Johne's disease is preventable if the sheep have the lick 365 days a year and the farmer makes sure that the sheep take it in some form or other, Johne's will not occur. The lick can be mixed with supplementary feed or spread on hay if necessary. Pastures must, of course, be remineralized at the same time so that the copper comes back into the food chain.

If an animal is affected and very valuable it can be cured by about nine days of massive vitamin supplementation comprised of vitamin C, vitamins B1, B12, B15 and VAM by injection. It is, after all, a disease that is only caused by bacteria. The sheep should also be fed on top quality, remineralized pasture at the same time.

Newman Turner, an organic farmer in the United Kingdom in the 1950s, who wrote three excellent books on pastures and farming, bought a condemned Jersey bull at a killer sale, used him over several cows and had him on the farm, mixing with his cattle, for about seven months until it died. Having got the cows in calf, he did not attempt to cure the bull and there was not a single case of Johne's infection in his herds then or later.

As Johne's is, in my experience, caused by a lack of copper, it will be noticed that black sheep succumb first. On a farm I was renting, the landlord sold his black poll cattle as they all caught Johne's disease. He brought in Herefords instead, and they survived because, being lighter colored, their copper requirements were lower. The sheep were also afflicted.

Lactation Tetany

All tetanies are basically primarily due to a deficiency of magnesium, with calcium implicated to a lesser degree. Hungerford says that the old treatment of calcium on its own works much better if magnesium is included as well, but it is only recently that this seems to have been realized. Stock that has been receiving supplementary magnesium and calcium in the form of the mineral licks should not succumb to lactation (or any other kind of) tetany.

The signs of lactation tetany are un-coordination followed very quickly by collapse and then, if nothing is done, death. This tetany can occur any time after lambing, especially on poor pasture that needs remineralizing. The sheep struggles in a circle and eventually dies. Treat her promptly with calcium and magnesium injections (available from any fodder store) used according to instructions and she will soon be back on her feet. With lactation tetany, basically the milk production of the ewe has used up the available calcium and magnesium and there is not enough left to sustain life. The condition could possibly be more common in milking sheep, but it is fairly rare in wool concerns.

Lambing Trauma

Occasionally after lambing a ewe will not get up for a few days. Make her comfortable by propping her up with a few bales of hay or straw. Feed and give her water, liquid kelp and cod-liver oil drench, and very often after a couple of days rest she will be back on her feet of her own volition. If she does not show any improvement within three weeks nerve damage, which is irreversible, may have occurred.

Laminitis

This is a form of founder and occurs in sheep fed too much protein either from the pasture or feed. They become lame and the feet will be hot. If you reduce the high protein immediately, making sure they get their dolomite, etc., in the licks, they will soon get over it. For stubborn individual cases give 100 grams of Epsom salts by drench three days running and a teaspoon of vitamin C, along with the same of dolomite daily. Analyze and remineralize the pastures. It always should be remembered that protein over 12 to 14 percent is going ultimately to cause trouble.

Lice and Exterior Parasites

Bad infestations are caused by malnutrition. This does not mean that the sheep are starving, but it does mean that the diet is unbalanced. Infested sheep will be seen scratching and rubbing themselves against fences, trees and so on, and must be in extreme discomfort, especially when the fleece is long. The presence of parasites detracts from the quality of the clip.

Lice are not very contagious. They only attack sheep that are deficient in sulfur. According to *CSIRO Rural Research Bulletin No. 22,* modern chemical farming practices have made sulfur unavailable in farm produce, so most of our feed is lacking in that necessary mineral. This can be fed in licks as already described. As long as the sulfur does not exceed 2 percent of all feed taken it is quite safe. If the supplementation is started at shearing time, the sheep should stay clear of infestation. If the sulfur is started when there is a good growth of fleece the lice tend to move out from the skin, but may be left dead in the wool, which can of course affect the clip.

If sheep are found to be lousy at shearing time, have a bucket of yellow dusting sulfur handy and run a handful down the back line of each sheep after shearing. This should take care of them until the sulfur comes through in the feed. Prevention is definitely better than cure with this one.

Liver Fluke (See Worms)

Maedi Visna

This is an autoimmune disease of sheep (and cattle) that fortunately is not present so far as is known in the antipodes. Like all similar conditions it is spread by blood transfer, but in goats it is also spread by milk and colostrum. It is, in effect, sheep (and cattle) AIDS. This is a serious problem in Europe. The goat version, CAE (caprine arthritis encephalitis), has been in Australia for many years and is spread by blood and milk; I found that when the copper levels of the herd were correct incidental infections did *not* occur (much the same was reported in the early days of AIDS).

Mastitis

This ailment is more expensive in sheep probably than any other breed of stock. This is usually because by the time its presence is discovered in a ewe, you have a wrecked udder and therefore a dead or dying lamb. It is quite easily controlled by ensuring that all the sheep get their share of dolomite and/or that the licks as mentioned are made available as well. For milking sheep it is essential that the pasture be analyzed to adjust the calcium and magnesium levels as well.

Milking sheep will need a teaspoon of dolomite per feed. If they are being bail fed twice a day, they need that amount each time. This especially applies if the bail feed is brought in as there will be a strong chance that it will be short of calcium and/or magnesium because this feed is generally grown with superphosphate and artificials. This would apply whether the farm paddocks were balanced or no.

If the pH of the ration is correct and the lactating ewe is getting her dolomite, the type of the mastitis organism seems to be immaterial. Even a torn udder will not produce instant mastitis, but of course the farmer should treat the tear and give the animal extra vitamin C and dolomite to offset any infection. If a ewe comes down with mastitis, give her a teaspoon of vitamin C powder and the same of dolomite (on top of what she gets in the bail) twice a day until the udder is clear; it will usually take two to three days.

To test for mastitis take a cup of water, add two drops of detergent and squirt some milk into the cup; if the milk coagulates or goes stringy, mastitis is present in some form or other.

In dairy herds peroxide is being used for bad cases of mastitis, such as black mastitis, that strike unexpectedly. Four drops of 6-percent hydrogen peroxide (from the chemist) in a syringe with four ml of clean water squirted into the affected quarter could be used for a sheep. Make sure to milk out the udder afterwards as much as possible; continue until the swelling and heat go down, which usually happens in less than 24 hours. Similar amounts, adjusted for size, have been used successfully in dairy cows.

It should be pointed out that the sheep must be receiving their normal copper in the lick or other method; mastitis in the United Kingdom did not clear up without the addition of this copper. The pastures in the United States and other countries have far higher natural protein than those in Australia.

Metritis

The signs of metritis are usually an evil-smelling discharge from the vulva following lambing, and it is more likely to occur if the lamb was born dead or taken away in pieces. If a vet is attending, he will insert a pessary, otherwise give a washout of a teaspoon of salt to two pints of water to remove the worst of the infective material (if the ewe sheds the afterbirth cleanly this should not be necessary).

Metritis and other conditions affecting the uterus are mainly caused by a lack of vitamin A. In drought or near drought weather there are often quite a few affected animals, as they will not have had enough green grass or sunlight to obtain the necessary vitamin A (and D) to carry them through the dry period. There will be a predisposition to metritis in stock on chemically manured paddocks as the chemicals inhibit the synthesis of vitamin A.

Any ewe with metritis should be put on A, D and E injections, or an A and D drench (cod-liver oil).

Vitamin C injections will also help clear up the infection, four to six grams (8 to 12 ml) by injection every other day, or a teaspoon a day orally. Unless the case is severe, a healthy ewe will often cure herself once the green feed comes away. She should not be put to the ram until she is clear and a swab can be taken when she is in season. Letting a ram cover an infected ewe can mean the and of his working life.

It is a wise precaution where any lamb is manually delivered to give a routine injection of 15 ml of vitamin C afterwards. Inject it into the neck muscle to help prevent any infection.

Milk Fever

This could be a problem in milking ewes that have been on poor paddocks and while it does not occur very often in farm sheep, it certainly could in dairy ewes. The signs are lethargy and uncoordination, and if the pupil of the eye is examined it will be found much dilated (milk fever is actually very like snake bite in its symptoms). It is caused by depletion of calcium and magnesium due to the ewe drawing on her reserves to fill her udder too quickly. The usual milk fever injection (make sure it contains calcium *and* magnesium) works very quickly and should, if possible, be given in four places for faster relief — each side of the shoulder and each side of the rump. Keep the ewe quiet for an hour or two after she has recovered. Milk fever is unlikely to arise on reminer-alized paddocks and/or where ewes have been given supplementary feed and the basic lick coming up to lambing.

As the signs for snake bite and milk fever are similar, the alternative should always be considered. If there is any doubt treat as for snakebite as well, it will do no harm. (I was once confronted by a horse in an advanced state of pneumonia and snake bite, luckily the same treatment — vitamin C by injection — worked for both.)

Navel Ill (See Arthritis, Infective)

Nasal Bots

This bot looks like a beetle larva without wings and is about three-quarters of an inch in length when fully grown. Sometimes one will hear sheep sneezing and find a nasal bot larva that has been ejected onto the ground. The egg is laid by the adult fly in the nostrils and there is much snorting when the flies are around. If the flock can be handled, putting a strong smelling eucalyptus-type ointment on the nose will often discourage flies, or make the sheep sneeze hard enough to dislodge the larva as it crawls up into the nasal passages.

This can be a serious condition if the animal is very young, as the nasal passages may not be large enough to accommodate the larva, in which case they migrate into the brain or elsewhere in the head. Usually in full-grown animals it runs its life cycle in the nasal passages, causing nothing more than discomfort. In the brain it can cause signs similar to circling disease, due to brain damage, in which case it is generally fatal.

Ophthalmia (See Pink Eye)

OS, Eperythrozoonosis
(Eperythrozoon ovis)

I first heard of this condition when working in Western Australia in April 1993. It is suspected that it is transferred by an insect such as a mosquito and/or by the blood transfer from an infected sheep. It is usually found in lambs and young weaners. Dr. Kevin Bell of the Wool Quality Project in western Australia says that he has never found it in older sheep, although it does not appear to be known whether they can be carriers without showing any signs of the condition.

The affected lamb will show anemia, with very pale mucous membranes and skin. Jaundice and hemoglobinuria (hemoglobin from red cell destruction being passed out in the urine, making it red in color) is sometimes seen, as well as an enlarged spleen and occasionally sudden death.

Lambs that fail to follow their dams when they are shifted can be a sign that they are affected. The disease runs a course of four to six weeks, and antibiotics such as tetracyclines are suggested. However it seems that vitamin B12 is a supportive therapy at a rate of two ml per patient. I also would suggest adding about half a ml of VAM (see appendix) and 10 ml of vitamin C at the same time (and in the same syringe). This could help the lamb recover, but it would not necessarily kill the organism or control the disease. Apparently Hungerford suggests this also — obviously an affected lamb could become a carrier when recovered. If sheep are not moved too much, deaths from this condition will be minimized. The exertion involved in yarding them to give the injection is enough to cause death.

Prevention in the form of sulfur (and the copper), which is in the basic lick, must be available to all and *no* molasses in any circumstances would go quite a way to stopping the mosquitos attacking. The molasses is undesirable because insects prefer to bite lambs or sheep that have sugar in the bloodstream. These kinds of insect outbreaks are worse on soils with a low pH. I think that when copper supplementation is correct the causative agent will not stay in the body anyway. Make sure the lick is available to all ages.

Pneumonia

All lung infections are made worse by below-optimum calcium and magnesium levels. Signs of pneumonia are labored and rapid breathing (see chart at the head of the chapter for normal breathing rates). If one listens to the animal's chest it sounds rather like an express train in a tunnel. A high temperature, misery and occasionally coughing will also be noticed.

This is a rare disease in sheep, and they would have to be in very poor condition for pneumonia to become a problem. Off-shears would be the only time they should be at risk. In milking or sharlee sheep that are kept yarded or confined there could be trouble. Sheds that are not properly ventilated can often be a contributing factor to a very rapid spread of pneumonia, especially the bacterial variety.

Even the viral kind of pneumonia can usually be controlled by making sure that the correct amount of dolomite (calcium and magnesium) is being fed, to which should be added extra vitamin A and D at a rate of at least two ml a day, and 10 grams (20 cc) of vitamin C by injection twice daily and the same by mouth (two heaped teaspoons) daily. Powdered vitamin E also should be given along with two cc of vitamin B12 a day for a fully grown sheep. Some firms market injectable vitamin E. Powdered vitamin E, known in Australia as White E, can be used orally and put in the food, the dosage is on the container. Vitamin E is invaluable for the convalescing pneumonia patient because it helps heal the lung damage. The extent of this damage can be gauged by checking the breathing rate and the vitamin E may be given for a week or two until the breathing rate improves.

Mycoplasma Pneumonia (Pleuro)

The dreaded pleuro (mycoplasma pneumonia) took its toll of sheep (and cattle) in the 1800s in Australia. Thousands of beasts died. Around 1995 I wrote that those days were over for Australia. But in May 1999, if calls received were anything to go by, it was alive and well in Western Australia in goats. It is highly contagious and for this reason alone any case of pneumonia should be checked out by a vet. The same nursing techniques could be tried, but mycoplasma pneumonia has a habit of recurring once the animal has contracted it, and a permanent cure seems to be very difficult to effect. Sheep that live in well-ventilated sheds where hygiene is correct, and that receive the right minerals should *not* be at risk, *but* remember that it is spread by coughing and sneezing and droplets can travel across a shed.

I remember going to inspect goats for export that were all shut in an airless and overheated shed. They were all infected, but had they been out in the field probably a fairly small number would have been affected.

If pleuro can be caught right at the outset and the drug erythromycin administered (by a vet), sometimes the organism can be killed — 15 ml of vitamin C and two ml of vitamin B12 should be given daily at the same time. If the disease has progressed for a few days shoot the animal because the disease will reoccur at intervals and ultimately kill the animal anyway — an expensive and painful process. Shooting and removal of the carcass is the only course if the pneumonia cannot be cured immediately.

Pregnancy Toxemia (Twin Lamb Disease)

This is an odd name for a condition that arises because the fetus, occasionally singular but generally twins, has taken all the necessary minerals and the ewe is left without enough to sustain life. It should not arise in well-kept flocks even with multiple births.

The signs of pregnancy toxemia are increasing lethargy; the pregnant ewe makes hard work about moving at all and finally refuses to do so. Exercise undoubtedly helps, as it dissipates the minerals that are available and keeps the gut working, but the time inevitably arrives when the minerals run out. Ewe and lambs will then soon die unless swift action is taken.

The quickest and most effective measure is to give a large drench (10 to 12 ml) of kelp, putting a teaspoon of dolomite in the mouth first. This seems to be highly effective and usually gets the ewe on her feet very quickly. The dose should be repeated daily for a few days and if the ewe is near lambing the dose could be continued until then and given a day or two after. Supportive injections of vitamin C with some vitamin B12 and VAM (two ml of each, see appendix) added will also help if the ewe was very low, and make sure she has access to the kelp ad lib as well. Again, this is a disease that should not arise if prenatal feeding includes having the lick out as well as grain or hay.

Pink Eye (Conjunctivitis, Ophthalmia, Sandy Blight)

Sheep that are wet around the eyes are often showing the first sign of this illness. Subsequently the eye clouds over and goes opaque. If treatment is not started promptly the eyeballs swell, ulcerate and burst, which is obviously very painful and apt to cause permanent blindness.

Pink eye is caused by an organism that only operates if the host is deficient in vitamin A. It is highly contagious for sheep who are deficient in that vitamin and the other minerals. In Australia, where huge areas are dry and without green feed for long periods, this can be a problem. It is made worse by the use of artificial fertilizers that inhibit all vitamins to a degree. Vitamin A is stored in the liver and there should, in theory, be enough from food consumption during the wet season to see a beast through the dry, but prolonged drought and, more importantly, poor land cause problems.

Geoff Wallace, the inventor of the Wallace Soil Conditioner, had a mob of bullocks on a poor paddock which contracted pink eye. He found that when they were moved onto one that was organic and in good heart, the pink eye cleared up in a few days.

To treat pink eye in sheep, the sufferers must be yarded, and the affected eyes can be treated by taking a 10 ml syringe, filling it with cod-liver oil and (without the needle, of course) putting two ml in each eye and the rest in the sheep's mouth. The affected sheep must be given a further dose of cod-liver oil, 10 ml, or an injection of A, D and E according to instructions on the bottle. Always use a fresh bottle, not a little that has been left from a previous time. Occasionally the bacteriostat goes bad after a while, so it is better to throw out a small amount left in the bottom of the bottle and use a fresh supply.

Plant Poisoning.

Poison plants are covered in Chapter 5 along with appropriate remedies.

Poisons

Chemical Poisoning

Poisoning due to chemicals is extremely difficult, if not impossible, to cure. Large quantities of vitamins A, B, E, C and the mineral zinc are suggested by Dr. Kalakerinos and the late Dr. Dettman for humans suffering from inorganic sprays or similar types of poisoning. These vitamins and zinc could be tried of animals if the animal showed some hope of living, and a few have actually been pulled through by this method.

Occasionally, just removing the cause is effective. Three goats from three different localities developed leukemia, which showed up as edema from the chin to the top of the forelegs. All of them had been in contact with pesticide sprays in various forms (one had been fed lucerne hay which was sprayed the day it was cut). Removing them from the source of contamination and feeding them good healthy food resulted in a complete remission in a couple of weeks. The University of Melbourne did the tests on these animals.

In all cases of suspect poisoning (except in the case of 1080, see below) it is always worth trying doses of both oral and injected vitamin C in fairly large quantities. Vitamin E is the other really useful vitamin for poisons, because of its healing action.

Arsenic

This poisoning produces a rather sweet smell in the mouth, extreme distress, vomiting (even in a ruminant) and a deathly chill. I have been told that ruminants die if they vomit, but I have managed to bring an animal through arsenic poisoning by using large doses of vitamin C both by injection and orally in combination with vitamins E and B12. Sadly, the exercise is not very productive as arsenic causes residual hormone and bone-marrow damage. The animal I saved was never very healthy again.

Lead

The usual cause is a lamb (more often than an adult) licking paint or old paint cans. This results in anemia, muscle weakness and diarrhea. Drenching with Epsom salts helps clear the system, and then the usual supportive measures should be followed. In the past this was quite a common form of poisoning in young calves. Vitamin C has been suggested as being quite effective for this type of poisoning. Sodium ascorbate by mouth, a teaspoon every two hours could be tried.

Mercury

This should be a thing of the past now that it has been banned as a silo fumigant. In its severe form it causes shredding of intestinal mucosa and diarrhea. In the subacute form, often caused by mercury-based latex paints, digestive disturbances such as loose teeth and salivation can be the signs. In either case, call a vet immediately and remove, if possible, the source of contamination. As in other cases of poisoning, supportive treatment with vitamins C and E will be of help.

Nitrate

This is mostly covered in the section on capeweed in Chapter 5. Nitrates are stored in broad leaved plants, even clover on occasion. In certain cases (drought-like weather with dry thunder storms is particularly bad) nitrates turn into the deadly nitrites in the gut. Normally nitrates are processed into proteins and amino acids in the plants by an enzyme called nitrate reductase. This process needs sunlight. In conditions of drought when there is a lot of cloud cover, the nitrates build up to dangerous levels turning to nitrites, which deplete the oxygen in the blood and the animal dies. On post mortem examination the blood appears completely black. At first, the symptoms are almost identical to tetanus. In fact, when my vet and I saw our first case it took us 24 hours to realize that it was something other than tetanus. According to Everist, writing in *Poisonous Plants in Australia*, huge doses of vitamin C are the only hope, but we did not find it worked. Giving ad lib kelp meal as well as the normal dolomite, etc., in the lick is the best and possibly the only strategy. The vets who worked with me to try and save the animals had no answer and we finally found that the above was the best way to go.

Phosphorus

This occurs after eating the old rat baits or similar types of poisons. The animal has a craving to drink and must not be allowed water in any form as this causes the phosphorus to react with the liquid and burn the intestines. If a phosphorus-poisoned animal has drunk water, it is kinder to put it out of its misery. White of egg, glucose and possibly a very little milk may be given at hourly intervals until the beast shows signs of recovery. This worked with a dog I knew — it took 36 non-stop hours — and I think it could possibly work with a sheep. In this type of poisoning, the breath of the animal also has a sickly sweet smell, quite unmistakable, and the sufferer is obviously feeling heat in its gut.

Prussic Acid

This is caused by eating young eucalypt shoots, usually from young sugar gum leaves. These grow in California and elsewhere in United States. The animal will foam at the mouth and go down. Drenching straight away with pharmaceutical chalk or fine dolomite (both in water) will effect an immediate recovery by neutralizing the poison. At least two tablespoons of chalk or dolomite to half a pint of liquid should work for a sheep.

1080 (Fluoroacetate, or 23 ppm Sodium Fluoride)

Glycerol monoacetate is the antidote, which is not normally carried by the veterinary profession. If 1080 poison is known to have been taken by a sheep (or a working dog), the antidote must be given within 20 minutes of the poison being taken. It will take approximately four hours for the patient to die after that, in great pain, and nothing can reverse it. Shooting is the only humane answer unless the antidote can be given in time. I am told by someone who worked in the Lands Department that 1080 does not cause pain. The vet to whom I took a neighbor's dog dying from it will back me up when I say that it certainly does cause *extreme* pain, at least in dogs.

Prolapse

This usually occurs before parturition and the signal symptom is that part of the placenta will obtrude from the vulva; this is generally more noticeable if the ewe is lying down. Lack of calcium is the primary cause of prolapse, due to lack of muscle tone, and can be cured by giving the animal calcium fluoride tablets over a period of two or three days (calcium fluoride is a cell salt and is nothing to do with the sodium fluoride in the water supply). The tablets are obtainable at any health shop. I would give a ewe 12 crushed tablets a day, and two days' dosage is usually enough. Do not on any account cut the prolapse, unless you want a dead animal. It should be pushed back gently, but it will generally not stay in while the muscle tone is too weak to hold it there.

There is a device which looks rather like a wire coat hanger, that is often suggested to hold in a prolapse, but it has a very poor running record. It often punctures the placenta before birth, resulting in the loss of the amniotic fluid (needed for lubrication as well as protection), and the ensuing dry birth usually means the loss of both ewe and lamb. Try calcium fluoride — I have seen it work several times with afflicted animals. Ewes on remineralized paddocks with adequate calcium and magnesium levels and with access to the lick should not suffer from prolapses.

Prolapse after Birth

The old folk practice used very successfully in the Herriot books was putting the prolapse back with four pounds of sugar. This worked for a cow, when no other remedy was successful (halve it for a sheep). The calcium fluoride would also be of help. This complaint does not seem to occur once the paddocks are correctly balanced and the mineral lick is obtainable. In milking goats I never saw it again once full remineralization was complete and the minerals were available in the feed.

Retained Afterbirth

This should not occur in an animal unless it is deficient in potassium and possibly selenium as well. Should there be an outbreak of this complaint you may suspect the latter deficiency. This would not occur in sheep on the lick and good healthy pastures, but they cannot assimilate selenium without sulfur, so if that is low amend it by top-dressing (usually with gypsum — calcium sulfate).

When an afterbirth is retained and the cervix has closed up, putrefaction can be prevented by injections of large doses of vitamin C. I had a goat that failed to pass an afterbirth due to trying unsuccessfully to produce two kids simultaneously in the middle of the night. By the time I extracted the dead kids, there was no chance of getting the afterbirth without being very rough or resorting to drugs. I gave her 10 grams of vitamin C by injection in the muscle three times during the day, and again next day. About a week later she was slightly off-color, so I repeated the treatment for two days, after which there was no more trouble and she produced quite normally next time around. Other people have also reported these results. A sheep could be treated in the same way.

Rickets

This is a disease that can affect lambs that are not getting the right amounts of calcium and magnesium in their diets, this may be due to several factors. Calcium and magnesium need vitamins A and D (cod-liver oil), as well as the minerals boron and copper to be fully assimilated, and a lack of any of these could be the cause of rickets. Lambs from sheep that have had licks out that contain dolomite, copper, sulfur and kelp should not be in trouble. Cod-liver oil should also be given.

Legs which bend under the weight of the body are a sign of rickets. Children from the slums in the 1800s often developed rickets to the point where they had to wear leg braces, mostly occasioned by the lack of sunlight and milk (vitamins A and D, calcium and magnesium) in their diets.

Very occasionally diets too high in phosphates, when too much grain or milk has been fed, can have the same effect by upsetting the phosphate to calcium/magnesium ratio. Giving young lambs too much milk can also produce this result as it suppresses the copper in the system.

Ringworm

Unless sheep are just off shears, this disease would be fairly unlikely to occur. It is a skin disease caused by a fungus, not a worm. The name originated because the fungus works in concentric rings and looks like a coiled worm. A wash of copper sulfate and cider vinegar, two tablespoons of each in a quarter of a pint of water and rubbed well into the lesions, usually effects a cure straight away. If not, repeat until all evidence is gone. Ringworm is only contagious when animals are deficient in copper. Cider vinegar rubbed well in several times will also effect a cure, and might be used if the ringworm was too near an eye to use the copper.

Scabby Mouth (Orf)

This is a herpes-based infection; it is a particularly fast-spreading and debilitating disease because as it spreads up from the mouth, the sheep is in too much pain to eat. It starts as a small scab by the mouth and quickly spreads all over the lower part of the face and can affect the feet and anywhere the mouth touches. The same wash as for ringworm works very quickly. Just dip the affected animal's face in the mixture and rub it well in; one or two applications are enough. It will not hurt them if they swallow a little, but take care it does not get in the eyes. Scabby mouth is highly contagious if animals are copper deficient, and this should be amended. Treat any lesions on the body or feet the same way, and make up feeds with about a tablespoon of the lick mixture per head per day for a week.

In 1998 a farmer in Northern England was particularly pleased when this cure worked so quickly because orf is regarded as an incurable and notifiable "plague" there. His vet rang and told me that the speed of the cure had impressed him enormously.

Scab (Soroptic Mange)

This was a dreaded disease in the past, but is now apparently unknown in Australia — although this is not the case in other countries. It is notifiable. Any suspect condition should be checked out by a vet, and a copper wash will not be a bad idea while waiting for professional help to arrive. I suspect scab is another manifestation of low copper levels. So many so-called illnesses just do not occur in properly supplemented sheep nowadays when they are receiving their free-take copper.

Scouring

Hungerford, in his work *The Diseases of Livestock*, says that unexplained scouring is often caused by a lack of copper in the diet. This has been found to be the case with young sheep on many occasions. One farmer with a large mob of scouring weaners that had not responded to worm drenches or anything for months, found that they recovered in a few hours after each was given 1.5 grams of copper sulfate in 10 grams of dolomite. This was administered as a dry powder straight into the mouth. A second dose could have been given next day if needed. He mixed the required amount of dolomite and copper sulfate really well, ran 500 weaners through the race, scooping up the right amount of the mixture and putting it in each animal's mouth. We do not use this method now as some farmers have used it even when sheep were on the lick, and no tests were done to see what the animals' copper status was first, creating the danger of overdosing the animals. However, ideally sheep must be fed via the lick, which is a balanced mixture, and the above scenario would not have occurred had they been on it. It is much easier to have it out than having to hand dose 500 weaners.

The type of scours is important to know; if it is just the normal manure in liquid form, it is not very serious. This can be caused by worms, therefore evidence of a copper shortage or just a simple acid/alkali imbalance. Quite often a large dose of dolomite, even powdered on the feed, can stop it. If it does not clear up one may, like Hungerford, assume a copper deficiency or worms. If a vet is handy it is not a bad idea to have a worm count done specifying the type, then you will have a guide for treating the rest of the flock.

Note: Many farmers in New Zealand use a very basic microscope to check for worms in their flocks — until the farm is fully on the right supplements, it is cheaper and less trouble to do this.

Scouring that is white, bubbly with gas, bloody or very offensive needs quick action. Give a teaspoon of sodium ascorbate powder and the same of dolomite by mouth every few hours to an adult sheep or hog, also 10 ml by injection every two hours. An oral dose of liquid kelp should be given once a day, and an injection of two ml of vitamin B12 (and VAM, see appendix) can have remarkable tonic effects, one dose should last several weeks. The cause of the scouring should be determined and if it is worms, the sheep could be given half a teaspoon of the lick mixture. But it is always preferable to mix the lick with some feed with the lick added on the top.

A rough rule of thumb is that lambs that scour under five weeks of age are short of magnesium (dolomite will work for this). After five weeks scouring is due to lack of copper, when the lick mixture will do equally well.

Any sheep being treated for debilitating scours should be kept quiet and have plenty of clean water available. As the condition gets better, bland food should be offered — no grain or lucerne hay — just plain oaten chaff, bran and grass hay if grazing is not available. Garlic in some form or other is very helpful for intestinal disturbances, vitaminized and given as a drench might be the easiest way if the sheep is not eating. It is important to remember that diarrhea, particularly in hot weather, dehydrates a sheep very fast. Water with 5-percent liquid kelp or similar with 5-percent cider vinegar could be left on offer.

Scrapie (See BSE)

Sheath Rot (Pizzle Rot)

Twenty years ago I was approached by a sheep farmer who was going organic and wanted to know what to do about this problem. I was rather at a loss, but I reckoned that it was possibly caused by a mineral deficiency affecting the pH of the system and the fields. I suggested he put out dolomite licks for the sheep. Nowadays I would have suggested giving the standard lick, as in Chapters 5 and 8 (according to the breed of the sheep). He rang me back a week or two later. He'd been kept busy replacing the licks, and the sheath rot had cleared up dramatically. All his conventional farming neighbors with the same problem were putting out their dolomite licks with equally satisfactory results, so it probably is caused by a pH and calcium/magnesium problem.

Sheep Pox

This is a herpes-based problem, which Massey reports is not often seen now. It could be a problem, however, especially in milking sheep. A copper wash, as for ringworm, applied topically will help the scabs dry up and drop off. Like most herpes-based infections, it does not occur in sheep or any other animals whose copper reserves are correct.

Snake Bite

Snake bite either kills immediately, or it takes an hour or more, according to the locality of the bite. Adult sheep are probably not at great risk owing to their wool. On a farm where tiger snakes were endemic, I never remember a sheep being bitten, but everything else was. However, I feel that lambs, which like all youngsters are very curious, might easily be bitten when investigating a basking snake. If found in time they can be saved.

The signs of snake bite are lack of coordination, collapse and very enlarged pupils. We are indebted to Dr. Klenner in the United States for discovering that vitamin C was a complete snake bite cure. The type of the snake is quite immaterial because the ascorbate detoxifies the venom, whatever the type.

Antivenin, apart from being expensive and the fact that one needs to know what type of snake has bitten, can also cause anaphylactic shock unless used almost immediately. I am told this is rare, but twice I have seen it after antivenin was used. Then it may become a case of the shock killing the animal, and not the snake, if no adrenalin is handy.

In areas where snakes are present the farmer should carry two or three bottles of injectable vitamin C (100 ml) in the fridge. Ten ml for lambs in the side of the neck repeated every two hours if necessary should effect a fairly rapid cure. Often one dose is enough, however, I prefer to give a follow up next day in case all the venom was not detoxified. An adult ram or ewe could be given 15 to 20 grams in the same way. One cannot overdose using vitamin C.

Spider Bites

Usually these are not so serious as snake or tick bites. Some spiders seem to cause swelling and extreme pain at the location of the bite, and vitamin C helps clear these up. If the actual site is known, rub some sodium ascorbate powder on it, as it stops the pain immediately (I found this out the hard way, when bitten myself). The most usual scenario, however, is a very swollen head or throat which usually takes two or three days to go down. The swelling is only serious if it is in the throat area and quick administration of ascorbate usually stops it becoming any worse, and ultimately stopping the air supply. Otherwise treat spider bites exactly like snake bites.

Tapeworm (See Worms)

Tender Wool

This is caused by a break in the nutritional value of the sheep's feed, and has been explained. There are not enough of the necessary minerals to keep the wool the same strength right along the staple. This can occur in the final stages of pregnancy, and shearing is often moved around so that the tenderness (or occasionally break) occurs at the top or bottom of the fleece, not in the middle. If sheep are supplied with their minerals on a regular basis, as in the aforementioned stock lick, farmers have assured me that they have had clips free of tender wool within a year.

Tetanus

The old name for tetanus was "lockjaw" because shortly after the onset of the illness, the jaw becomes locked. The sheep will appear staggery and disunited, and if hit smartly under the chin, the eyes will roll backwards.

Tetanus is caused by *Clostridium tetanae*, a clostridial bacteria that proliferates in deep airless wounds that have not been disinfected properly (often because they are not even visible). The symptoms usually do not appear until 10 days after the wound. Pierce wounds that cannot be seen, from rusty nails or bullet wounds (as from stray lead shot), are all particularly dangerous. Shearing cuts could occasionally cause it if untreated.

The tetanus organism is generally present in soil where stock of any kind have been running. It used to be associated with horses, but it can occur with any animal, so all wounds must be thoroughly disinfected. Vitamin C must be given after a possible tetanus-prone wound until all danger is passed — at least 14 days. Do not think that the five-in-one vaccination means that tetanus cannot occur, because if conditions are bad enough it can and does.

Tetanus is a horrible disease which takes several weeks to run its course. The animal is in a nervous and painful state with a high fever, and the slightest noise causes it to go into convulsions. Top-class nursing was the only hope prior to the use of vitamin C. I have helped bring a horse through the disease before the days of vitamin C.

Using vitamin C, the locked jaws will relax in 10 to 20 minutes; 30 ml should be given by intramuscular injection in the neck, as the animal cannot swallow. If this is given the moment the signs are noticed, the patient is usually well on the way to recovery within three or four hours. Obviously it would have to be a very valuable stud animal for most people to take the measures suggested above. If the tetanus is advanced, keep giving 30 ml every few hours until the animal relaxes and starts to improve. Then the dose, as a heaped teaspoon of sodium ascorbate, can be given orally in liquid twice a day for a few days.

Once the sheep is up and about, just keep an eye on it. Light, nourishing food and required minerals should complete the cure. The sooner tetanus is treated the more rapid the recovery, do not expect to leave it several days and then expect a good result. It is *very* painful.

Tick Bite

Vitamin C works well for tick bite, too, even in cases where the sheep is already in a coma. Give it as indicated for snake bite. If the sheep is unconscious, take care when giving it orally that it does not go down the windpipe. Find the tick(s) if possible and remove them by putting tea-tree oil or similar on them. If the tick(s) have been on a lamb for several days, it is probably better to put the lamb down, as the venom seems to cause residual after effects in these cases. Perseverance with vitamin C, first by injection (15 ml) and then orally as a heaped teaspoon, has occasionally worked.

Note: The more sour and unbalanced the land, the greater the tick problem. Make sure that the land is analyzed and brought into balance.

Toxoplasmosis

This is a disease that does not seem to occur in sheep that are on the stock licks. It is due to feed contamination when cats have been around, and it causes abortion and/or dead lambs. It could be a problem in housed sheep and in dairies — and certainly used to be until I discovered that it — like all similar conditions — did not occur once we learned to incorporate copper in the diets.

Once a sheep has lost lambs due to this cause, it is immune to further infestation. It would be more likely to affect dairy setups where the sheep were fed inside, but I consider it is another condition that we do not hear of now in properly fed and supplemented sheep. It is a zoonose, and pregnant humans can catch the organism from contact and abort their babies, so care should always be taken when handling a dead fetus (or any sick animal) or cat litter boxes.

Water Belly (Stones, Urinary Calculi)

These can be a real problem in areas where the water supply is from a highly mineralized bore. Rams and wethers are especially susceptible due to their long, narrow ureter, unlike the wider one of the ewe that cannot be so easily blocked. However, if some way can be found of including a little cider vinegar in the food, stones do not occur. The amount of vinegar needed is surprisingly small — for a ram a teaspoon every few days would be enough. Farmers also tell me that when the lick is out all the time, water belly does not occur. It is a condition due in part to a calcium and magnesium imbalance.

Affected animals show signs of pain when trying to pass water, and in some cases the pain can be so great the sheep will become very ill. Definitely a case of prevention being much easier than cure, the latter is almost impossible in a ram, or wether. Sometimes a ewe can be persuaded to pass a stone as her ureter is wider and shorter than that of the male.

Warts

I have never heard of warts on a wool sheep, but they could occur on the bare parts of the body in natural wool shedders, for example, around eyelids, lips, sheaths or udders. Warts are caused by a virus, which apparently is only interested in a magnesium-deficient host. Extra dolomite in some form or other is enough to halt the progress of warts, eventually making them drop off. Actually, magnesium and vitamin C are needed, but as sheep would have enough vitamin C in their system (read the section on vitamin C), it would not have to be supplemented.

White Muscle Disease

This affects young lambs who are deficient in selenium. Lambs become lethargic and unable to move. Give some vitamin E in any form until the vet can come; if the animals immediately get better, it will confirm that it is indeed white muscle disease. Feeding kelp on a regular basis is often enough to stop this ailment from occurring. Kelp contains selenium in natural form, but sulfur is also needed because without the amino acids of sulfur, selenium cannot be assimilated. Seeing that the sheep have access to and/or are fed the lick is the best remedy.

Note: Nearly all of the diseases listed are due to bad management and/or mineral imbalances. Anyone reading through the list will understand that if the standard lick mentioned at the start of the section is always available, and the fields are being regenerated where possible, few, if any of these conditions (barring accidents) should occur.

Chapter 11

Worms — Another Strategy

Given the information in Chapter 8 in the section on copper, where it is pointed out that Dr. William A. Albrecht found that worm infestations (of any kind) only occurred in copper-deficient animals, the section below on different kinds of worms is academic. This section should not really be necessary on a well run farm.

It has been noticeable with all stock that fluke, tapeworm and coccidia are the first and easiest to prevent even with quite small amounts of copper. Those farmers with sheep on the lick described in Chapter 8 will find that drenching becomes a thing of the past. A worm count of 200 or below is not a concern in properly supplemented and fed animals. This has now been shown on a number of farms. Not only actual worms, but all protozoa-type of infections also seem to be caused by a lack of copper in the diet. It took me and other farmers a few years to realize that many conditions, such as coccidia and possibly toxoplasmosis, just were not occurring once the ration was in order.

Drenches are not the answer to worms, the answer lies in the good husbandry that has been outlined in earlier chapters. Nowadays there is drench resistance to nearly every brand of proprietary drench excepting the newest ones, and they will inevitably succumb. Using a natural system of farming that lets the dung beetles, earthworms and soil fauna keep parasitic organisms down below the surface of the soil for us is the answer. The copper in the lick prevents the worms from staying in the sheep's gut, they die out fairly quickly because they have to live inside a beast to complete their life cycle, and the copper makes that impossible. It is interesting that worm counts done soon after sheep arrive on a farm often show quite high count of eggs, but no adults, either mature or immature — another week or two on the lick is probably enough to see the animals fully clear. When hatched, worms just do not stay in an animal whose copper reserves are correct.

Copper and Worms

I have not used any proprietary drenches for 35 years now. Copper sulfate with various additions was used for many years prior to the advent of artificial chemical drenches in the late 1950s. The copper was mixed with either carbon tetrachloride (a very poisonous cleaning fluid), lead arsenate (another dangerous poison) or nicotine sulfate, which was possibly the safest of the three. I very much doubt if the reported deaths were due to copper poisoning.

Copper toxicity causes liver damage, which, if not treated, is fatal. However, we now know that when copper is administered with dolomite, there is little risk of copper poisoning unless the sheep have been grazing heliotrope or some other weed high in copper, such as Patterson's Curse or St. John's wort; if they had, however, the chance of a worm burden would be virtually nil because of the high copper content of all three.

According to the Department of Primary Industry in Queensland, the blood serum levels of copper in a sheep should be between 500 and 1,100 milliliters per liter, at which levels worm infestations would be unlikely. In all cases of suspected worm infestation a count should be taken, either by the vet or, as many farmers the world over these days do, by examining the manure with a microscope (nothing fancy, the sort used in schools will do).

Longstanding copper overload can apparently be corrected by giving the affected sheep dolomite on a permanent basis, with an injection of vitamin B15 (sometimes sold under the trade name of DADA), Pangamic acid (two cc) and vitamin C (eight cc) in the same syringe once a week. This has been tried in the field on farms where too much copper has been spread on the land. For immediate copper poisoning give the sheep a teaspoon of dolomite and vitamin C powder by mouth every few hours, and two cc of vitamin B15 with 10 cc of sodium ascorbate (vitamin C) in the same syringe by injection. This can be given every few hours, although a calf that I first did this work on recovered fully in an hour and a half and further doses were not necessary. Signs of copper poisoning are misery and a hunched-up appearance — in effect acute bellyache due to liver pain.

According to Justine Glass, black animals need about six times as much copper as white ones. Merinos need roughly the same amount as black animals depending on the density and fineness of the fleece (the 2.5 times the amount of follicles per square inch found on the Merino in comparison to most crossbred sheep, puts the Merino in this category). In days gone by, shepherds would run a black sheep with their flocks and when these turned light brown, white or striped, they knew that they had to supplement the sheep with copper. Sheep masters have always and still do use this mineral to improve the appearance of their show animals' fleeces.

Initially several friends who ran cattle, horses, sheep or goats experimented using copper instead of proprietary drenches, with very satisfactory results. The only controlled experiment was performed with goats, with the Department of Agriculture (Victoria, Australia) doing the tests. Half were given the latest "state of the art" drench (not the Ivermectin group), and half were given the copper sulfate/dolomite/vitamin C dose. The results were equal — 100 percent clear in both cases.

When I first started using copper sulfate instead of proprietary drenches there did not appear to be any guidelines, and Dr. Albrecht, whose works show that copper prevents worm infestations, does not mention amounts. A retired vet lent me a copy of the *British Veterinary Codex* (1952), from which a great many vets worldwide were taught, and which allowed me to work out amounts. I had reckoned that monogastrics need about half the amount on body weight that ruminants require; however, work done by the University of Minnesota on ponies and copper requirements suggests that equines actually top the list as far as copper requirement and/or tolerance goes.

I have discussed running copper through the diet with various vets, and at least one did not have apoplexy, but was genuinely impressed and interested because to use his exact words: "We have come to the end of the line with proprietary drenches." That was

18 years ago, and the situation has not improved with the years. (Note that three grams of copper sulfate is about equal to a teaspoon measure.)

A farmer in the western district of Victoria, Australia, started to feed his Merinos on the stock lick mentioned above and had one or two slightly surprising occurrences. I had always wondered why goats became sexually active at about four months or younger and sheep apparently did not do so until they were a year old. We soon found out — his young ewes, which normally were not separated from the ram lambs until they were a year old, dropped their lambs at a year old. The only reason the sheep had not been sexually active before was due to the lack of copper in the food chain.

His vet, on a routine visit suddenly realized that the ewe lambs had their lambs at foot, and was quite appalled. Much too young, but, as the farmer pointed out, they actually looked considerably better than the two-year-old breeders, having been on the correct minerals virtually from birth. The vet took worm samples and said he would get back to the farmer. He rang in and said they had 200 worm eggs per gram, but no immature or adult worms. The vet asked the farmer, "What are you going to do about that?" The reply was: "Nothing. If they look that good with those worms, they can jolly well keep them." What neither realized is that those eggs would not mature, as the copper in the system would prevent it.

Varieties of Worms

The following list outlines the chief culprits in interior parasites. Farmers should know their habits, even if they are to become a thing of the past.

Barber's Pole Worm (Haemonchus contortus)

This causes as much havoc in Europe as it does here and is certainly the most insidious and dangerous on the list. This is a blood-sucking worm that can be picked up and carried in encapsulated form in cold weather until the time is right for it to emerge in the animals gut and wreak havoc. It is particularly deadly to lambs, and kills by totally robbing them of blood. It waits for a really hot spell to emerge, when it causes almost total anemia very quickly. Drenching when it is in the encapsulated form does not work, so it is necessary to drench the moment a young animal's lower eyelids become pale (a sign of anemia). By the time the eyelids are white, it is usually too late. This is yet another case where prevention in the form of good farming practice involving licks being available would be the best strategy. The copper in the licks would have prevented the Barber's Pole Worm from moving in from the start.

Brown Stomach Worm (Ostertagia)

Another blood-sucking worm, but this can be destroyed whenever the animal is drenched. Quite often two drenches are needed on successive days, as the worm burrows into the stomach walls, and does not come out until those at large have been destroyed by the first drench. One full-grown Alpine buck goat that I bought that weighed in at about 400 pounds actually needed three days of drenching before he was clear; he arrived looking terrible.

Coccidiosis

This does not occur in sheep or any other stock whose mineral supplementation is correct. Blood in the feces and ill thrift are a mark of the illness.

Lung worm (Meullerius capillaris and Dirofilaria immitis)

There are two distinct sort of lung worm, and these used to need two different drenches. Signs of lung worm infestation are coughing and ill thrift, and a worm count will be needed to determine that kind of lung worm unless you plan on using the Ivermectin group of wormers. Lung worm, if not dealt with, causes lasting damage and quite often really healthy looking animals with slight coughs have lung worm scarring. Nothing much can be done about these cases except trying vitamin E on them.

Note: Using a severe drench on bad a lung worm case can be fatal because all the worms in the lungs will be killed and there will not be enough room left for the sheep to gain the oxygen it needs, so it virtually dies of mechanical pneumonia. The lick would be the best way of moving them on fairly painlessly. Better in this case to use a mild drench that deals with the worms in the intestines (part of the lung worm's cycle is spent there), and then a day or two later use something that will kill those left in the lungs, some of which will have migrated by then.

Pin Worms (Nematodes)

These are probably often carried by sheep without the farmer being aware of their presence. If a young lamb seems off-color, examine it around the anus where these worms may be seen wriggling around. A lot of tail wagging can be a sign of their presence. A Piperizane drench will be needed to get rid of them, the normal drenches do not usually touch them. Piperizane powder, which is used for poultry, will work and the dosage can be determined from the container. These worms do not stay around if the copper levels are correct.

Tapeworm (Monezia expanza)

There is some controversy on tapeworms. Some authorities say they are species specific, in other words, a sheep could not pick up tapeworms from a dog, but others say this is rubbish. Tapeworms in sheep are possibly more common than is generally realized, indicating that perhaps they do cross between species. If tapeworms are present, the white segments can be seen in manure and often the animal is very potbellied.

Some of the drenches that claim to affect all interior parasites do not touch tapeworm, as a farmer discovered after dosing some hoggetts with all available drenches, and which were still slightly below par. He gave them copper and dolomite in a mixture I advised him to use. There was considerable surprise when an appreciable number of them discharged several feet of tapeworm. If using a proprietary drench, your vet will advise.

Liver Fluke (Fasciola hepatica)

Liver fluke has a six-week life cycle that starts as a small, conical snail whose larvae infect the stock. These can infest very wet land or dams and, once they have been ingested, grow into a full-grown (about one-half inch wide) fluke in the sheep's liver.

Fluke can be also be eliminated from dams by putting about a pound of copper sulfate into an average acre dam, more into a larger one. Too much copper, and all the fresh water prawns will be killed.

If fluke are infesting wet land, which is quite usual, although it is not often realized that fluke can be present without water, supplementing the stock with copper sulfate will be the only answer.

Analyzing and top-dressing with the necessary lime minerals will stop a sour paddock from harboring fluke snails.

Another source of liver fluke is irrigation systems, as the snail comes in with the water. Sometimes farmers put a very thick canvas bag containing a little copper sulfate at the water outlet/inlet to make sure the larvae or snails do not survive.

Signs of liver fluke are anemia, ill thrift, occasionally a swelling under the jaw and a capricious appetite. Liver fluke drenches are very expensive, and rather severe, raising the copper in the ration until the eyelids become a deep pink will send the fluke on their way. Small doses of copper, as would be gained from having the stock lick in Chapter 8, are all that is necessary for a sure preventative.

The bottom line for all these creatures is *prevention*. Make sure that the sheep have their lick either free take or mixed with food, and drenching should *not* be necessary. Four grams of the lick mix per day per head would be a starting point if hand feeding, as in dairy sheep set-ups. The final bottom line is to have the land on which the sheep live in such good heart that the various minerals will be available in the feed, and the lick will be there solely as a back-up.

Selected Sources

Acres U.S.A., P.O. Box 91299, Austin, TX 78709, orders only 1-800-355-5313 (various articles).

Adams, Ruth. *Complete Home Guide to All Vitamins.* Larchmont Books, New York, 1971.

Albrecht, Dr. William A. *The Albrecht Papers*, vols. 1-4. Charles Walters, ed. Acres U.S.A., Austin, TX, 2004.

Allenstein, I.C., *et al.* "Moulds Are Causing Feeding Problems," *Hoard's Dairyman*, 1993.

Auerbach, Charlotte. *Science of Genetics,* revised edition. Hutchinson Press, London, 1969.

Baïracli-Levy, Juliette de. *Herbal Handbook for Farm and Stable.* Faber and Faber, London, 1952.

Balfour, Lady Eve. *The Living Soil and the Haughley Experiment.* Universe Books, New York, 1976.

Béchamp, Antoine. *The Blood and Its Third Anatomical Element.* Veritas Press, Queensland, 1988.

Begley, Sharon. "The End of Antibiotics." *Newseek,* 1994.

Bellfield, Wendell O. "Megascorbic Prophylaxis and Megascrobic Therapy: A New Modality in Preventative Medicine," *Journal of the International Academy of Preventative Medicine*, volume 11, no. 3.

Blood, D.C., J.A. Henderson, and O.M. Radostits. *Veterinary Medicine*. Baillierre Tyndal Press, London and Sydney, 1979.

Bromfield, Louis. *Malabar Farm*. Cassell, London, 1949.

Buist, Robert. *Orotates, Mineral Salts of Vitamin B13*. Self-published, 1978.

Burdon's Microbiology, 5th edition. Collier-Macmillan, New York, 1967.

Callahan, Philip S. *Paramagnetism*. Acres U.S.A., Austin, TX, 1995.

Carter, H.B. *His Majesty's Spanish Flock*. Angus and Robertson, Sydney, 1964.

Carson, Rachel. *Silent Spring*. Hamish Hamilton, London, 1964.

Cetinkaya, B., *et al.* "Relationship Between the Presence of Johne's Disease and Farm Management Factors in Dairy Cattle in England," in *Preventative Veterinary Medicine*, 32, 1997.

Coleby, Pat. *Natural Cattle Care*. Acres U.S.A., Austin, TX, 2001.

Coleby, Pat. *Healthy Cattle Naturally*. Landlinks Press, Melbourne, 2002.

CSIRO Rural Research Bulletins. No. 22 and others, quarterly publication, Melbourne.

Curr, Edward M. *Recollections of Squatting in Victoria*. Melbourne University Press, 1963.

Darwin, Charles. *Darwin on Humus and the Earthworm*. Faber and Faber, London, 1881.

Davis, Adelle. *Let's Get Well*. George Allen and Unwin, London, 1966.

Davis, J.B. *Proceedings of the 6th Beef Forum*. University of Adelaide, 1993.

Dettman, Glen, Archie Kalokerinos, and Ian Dettman. *Vitamin C: Nature's Miraculous Healing Missile*. Frederick Todd Publishing, Melbourne, 1993.

Dettman, Glen and Archie Kalokerinos. "Vitamin C and Cancer." Transcript of an address given to the International Association of Cancer Victims and Friends, March 31, 1979.

Dowling, Ralph and Ross A. Mackenzie. *Poisonous Plants: A Field Guide*. Department of Primary Industries, Brisbane, 1993.

Emsley, John. *The Shocking History of Phosphorus: A Biography of the Devil's Element*. Pan Books, London, 2000.

Evans, William, ed. *Diary of a Welsh Swagman, 1869-1894*. Griffin Press, Adelaide, 1975.

Everist, Selwyn P. *Poisonous Plants*. Angus and Robertson, 1981.

Farmer's Weekly, Anthelmintic Supplement, May 1997.

Glass, Justine. *The Earth Heals Everything: The Story of Biochemistry*. Peter Owen, London, 1958.

Goodman, Louis S. and Alfred Gillman. *Pharmacological Basis of Therapeutics*, 5th edition. New York, 1975.

Graham, Frank, Jr. *Since Silent Spring*. Fawcett World Library, Connecticut, 1970.

Gregg Charles T. *The Plague: An Ancient Disease in the Twentieth Century*, revised edition. University of New Mexico Press, 1986.

Grieve, Mrs. M. *A Modern Herbal*. Penguin Books, London, 1976.

Hayes, Horace. *Veterinary Notes for Horse Owners*, 7th edition. Hurst and Blackett, 1903.

Hensel, Julius. *Bread from Stones*. Acres U.S.A., Metairie, Louisiana, 1991.

Howard, Sir Albert. *An Agricultural Testament*. Oxford University Press, New York and London, 1943.

Howard, Sir Albert. *Farming and Gardening for Health or Disease*. Faber and Faber, London, 1940.

Hubbard, C.E. *Grasses*. Penguin Books, London, 1972.

Humphrys, John. *The Great Food Gamble*. Hodder and Stoughton, London, 2001.

Hungerford, T. *Diseases of Livestock*, 8th edition. McGraw-Hill, Sydney, 1951.

Hussey B.M.J., *et al. Western Weeds.* Plant Protection Society of Western Australia, 1997.

Jarvis, D. C. *Folk Medicine.* Lion Publishers, London, 1958.

Jensen, Bernard and Mark Anderson. *Empty Harvest.* Pavely Publishing Group, Garden City, NY, 1973.

Jensen, Bernard. *Goat's Milk Magic.* Self-published, Escondido, CA, 1994.

Johnson, Clarence. "20-Day Shelf Life in Fluid Milk," *American Dairy Review,* July 1979.

Kalokerinos, Archie. *Every Second Child.* Thomas Nelson, Australia, 1974.

Kelly, Robin A. *The Sky Was Their Roof.* Andrew Melrose, London, New York and Toronto, 1955.

Kervran, C. Louis. *Biological Transmutations and Their Application in Chemistry, Physics, Biology, Ecology, Medicine, Nutrition, Agronomy and Geology.* Happiness Press, California, 1966.

Kessler, J. "Elements Mineraux Chez le Chevre, Donne de Base et Apports Recommands." Paper presented at ITOVIC INRA International Symposium on Feeding Systems for Goats, Tours, France, 1981.

King, F.C. *The Weed Problem: A New Approach.* Faber and Faber, London, 1951.

Kinsey, Neal, and Charles Walters. *Hands-On Agronomy.* Acres U.S.A., Austin, TX, 1993.

Klenner, Frederick R. "Observations on Dose and Administration of Ascorbic Acid When Employed Beyond the Range of a Vitamin in Human Pathology," *Journal of Applied Nutrition,* Winter 1971, pp. 61-87.

Lisle, Harvey. *Enlivened Rock Powders.* Acres U.S.A., Austin, TX, 1994.

Mackenzie, David. *Goat Husbandry.* Faber and Faber, London, 1957. [Note: Later editions of this text recommend the use of unnecessary drugs. Only this first edition is suitable from a standpoint of natural husbandry.]

Marston, Hedley. "The Utilization of Sulphur by Animals, with Special Reference to Wool Production," *CSIRO Rural Research Bulletin*, No. 39, Melbourne, 1928.

Massy, Charles. *Australian Merino*. Penguin Books, Australia, 1990.

McCabe, Ed. *Oxygen Therapies: A New Way to Approach Disease*. Energy Publications, Morrisville, NY, 1988.

McDonough, Ed. *Clinic*. Platinum Pen Publishing Inc., Kansas City, MO, 1991.

McKenzie, Ross A. and Ralph M. Dowling. *Poisonous Plants, A Field Guide*. Information Series, no. Q192035, Department of Primary Industries, University of Queensland, Brisbane, 1993.

MacLeod, George. *A Veterinary Materia Medica and Clinical Repertory*. C. W. Daniel, Saffron, Walden, UK, 1995.

Mollison, Bill. *Permaculture*. Tagari Publications, New South Wales, 1997.

Moore, James. *Outlines of Veterinary Homeopathy for Horse, Cow, Dog, Sheep and Hog Diseases*, 7th edition. Henry Turner, London, 1874.

Moskowveitch, Richard. "Immunisations, A Dissenting View," Lecture 8 from *Dissent in Medicine, Nine Doctors Speak Out*. New Medical Foundation, Contemporary Books, Chicago, 1984.

Neilsen, Forrest H. "Boron, an Overlooked Element of Potential Nutritional Importance," *Nutrition Today*. January/February 1988.

Nick, Gina L. "Medicinal Properties in Whole Foods," *Townsend Letter for Doctors*, May 2003.

Notman, G. Claude. *Of Sheep and Men*. Waller and Chester, Ballarat, 1981.

Passwaters, Richard A. *Selenium as Food and Medicine, What You Need to Know*. Keats Publishing, New Canaan, Connecticut, 1980.

Periam, Jonathon, and A.H. Baker. *The New Pictorial Cyclopedia of Livestock and Complete Stock Doctor*. David McRae Publishing, Melbourne, 1901.

Prusiner, Stanley. 'Prions," *Scientific American*, October 1984.

Purdey, Mark. *Ecosystems Supporting Clusters of Sporadic TSE's Demonstrate Excesses of the Radical-Generating Divalent Cation Manganeses and Deficiencies of Co-Factors Cu, Se, Fe, Zn. Medical Hypotheses.* Harcourt Medical Publishers, 2000.

Rainsford, K.D., *et al. Copper and Zinc in Inflammatory and Degenerative Diseases.* Kluwer Academic Publishers, Dordrecht/Boston/London, 1998.

Reynolds, E.F. *The Extra Pharmacopoeia,* 28th edition. Pharmaceutical Press, London, 1982.

Russel, Mark, Don Scott, and William Hope. "Moldy Corn Poisoning in Horses." *Acres U.S.A.,* February 1995.

Schutte, Karl H. *The Biology of Trace Elements.* Crosby Lockwood and Son, London, 1964.

Sinclair, H.M., ed., *The Works of Sir Robert McCarrison.* Faber and Faber, London, 1952.

Short, Kate Hughes. *Quick Poison, Slow Poison.* Envirobook, Sydney, 1994.

Soil Association Journal. Various issues, 1956-1960, published in Great Britain.

Stone, Irwin T. *The Healing Factor: Vitamin C Against Disease.* Grosset and Dunlap, New York, 1974.

Sturtevant Engineering. *Modern Manufacture of Chemical Manures.* Sturtevant Enginering Co., Ltd., London, 1920.

Turner, Newman. *Fertility Farming.* Faber and Faber, London, 1950.

Udzal, F.A., and W.R. Kelly, "Entero Toxaemia (Pulpy Kidney) Disease of Goats." Paper given at seminar, Department of Veterinary Pathology, Queensland University, Banyo Conference Centre, Brisbane, Queensland, 1996.

Voisin, André. *Grass Productivity,* Island Press, Washington, DC, 1959.

Voisin, André. *Soil, Grass and Cancer.* Acres U.S.A., Austin, TX, 2000.

Wallach, Joel and Ma Lan. *Let's Play Doctor.* Double Happiness Publishing, California, 1997.

Wallach, Joel and Ma Lan. *Let's Play Herbal Doctor.* Wellness Publishing Co., Bonita, CA, 2001.

Walters, Charles. *Fletcher Sims' Compost.* Acres U.S.A., Austin, TX, 1993.

Walters, Charles. *Weeds: Control without Poisons.* Acres U.S.A., Austin, TX, 1996.

Walters, Charles. *Eco-Farm: An Acres U.S.A. Primer.* Acres U.S.A., Austin, TX, 2003.

Whitby, Coralie. "How Do Soils Affect Our Diet?" Talk presented to the Orthomolecular Association of Australia Seminar, June 25, 1982.

Willis, Harold. "Roots," *Acres U.S.A.,* December 1994.

Yeomans, P.A. *The Challenge of Landscape: The Development and Practice of Keyline.* Keyline Publishing, Sydney, 1958.

Yeomans, P.A. *Water for Every Farm.* Keyline Publishing, Sydney, Australia, 1971.

Yiamouyiannis, John. *Fluoride: The Aging Factor.* Health Action Press, Delaware, OH, 1993.

Selected Resource Suppliers

The following firms supply many of the materials Pat Coleby recommends.

Agri-Dynamics

Agri-Dynamics produces natural formulations for livestock, equine, pets and aqua-culture using botanicals, essential oils, nutriceuticals, chelated and colloidal minerals. Agri-Dynamics, P.O. Box 735, Easton, Pennsylvania 18044, phone (610) 250-9280, fax (610) 250-0935, website www.agri-dynamics.com.

Countryside Natural Products, Inc.

Countryside Natural Products, Inc. is a source for natural products for healthy soil, plants and animals, including Redmond NTM salt, Maxicrop, free-choice minerals, kelp and more. Countryside Natural Products, Inc., 1688 Jefferson Highway, Fishersville, Virginia 22939, phone 888-699-7088 or (804) 365-8738), fax (804) 365-7889, website www.countrysidenatural.com.

Crystal Creek

Crystal Creek offers natural animal health products and programs for dairy, beef, calf, goat, sheep and horse producers. Crystal Creek, N. 9466 Lakeside Road, Trego, Wisconsin 54888, phone 888-376-6777, fax (715) 466-5042, website www.crystalcreeknatural.com.

The Fertrell Company

Fertrell is a source for organic fertilizers and soil conditioners used for nurseries, gardening, lawns, houseplants and farms. Fertrell also offers a full line of products and services necessary for proper livestock management and nutrition. Fertrell Company, P.O. Box 265, Bainbridge, Pennsylvania 17502, phone (717) 367-1566, fax (717) 367-9319, website www.fertrell.com.

Helfter Feeds, Inc.

Helfter Feeds, Inc. is certified as a processor and handler of organic livestock supplementation and ingredients. Helfter Feeds, Inc., P.O. Box 266, Osco, Illinois 61274, phone: 866-435-3837 or (309) 522-5024, fax (309) 522-5021, website www.helfterfeeds.com.

Midwestern Bio-Ag

Midwestern Bio-Ag is a biologically based agri-consulting company offering biological and organic consulting services as well as soil and livestock products. Midwestern Bio-Ag, P.O. Box 160, Blue Mounds, Wisconsin 53517, phone 800-327-6012, fax (608) 437-4441, website www.midwesternbioag.com.

Metric Conversions

Liner Measurement

Meters x 3.281 = Feet

Meters x 39.37 = Inches

Centimeters / 2.540 = Inches

Kilometers / 1.609 = Miles

Weights & Volume

Liters / 3.785 = Gallons

Liters / 0.9463 = Quarts

Liters / 0.02957 = Ounces

Grams / 28.349 = Ounces

Kilograms / 0.4536 = Pounds

Liters x 1000 = Cu. Centimeter

Area

1 Sq. Kilometer x 247.105 = Acres

1 Sq. Meter x 1.19599 = Sq. Yards

Index

nicotine sulfate, 186
nitrate poisoning, 59
nitrates, 95, 173
nitrogen, 64, 70, 74
nitrogenous fertilizers, 28, 48
North Otago, NZ, 17
Northern England, 25
Northern Europe, 21
Notman, Claude, 4, 8
nut trees, 73, 91
nuts, 61

oaten chaff, 178
oaten hay, 39, 40
oats, 49
Of Sheep and Men, 4, 8
ointments, 3
oleander, 54, 57
oleander poisoning, 59
onions, 130
Orbell, C.N., 17
organic manure, 106
orotic acid (see vitamin B13)
OS (eperythrozoonosis), 167-68
Ovis montana, 7
oxalate, 56, 59
oxalic acid, 58
Oxfordshire Downs, 22

PABA (para-aminobenzoic acid), 119
pangamic acid, 122-23, 186
pangola, 56
pantothenic acid, 3, 121
paraffin, 126
paralysis, 121
parasites, 4, 72, 112
Paris, 7, 8
parrots, 123
parsley, 131
Passwater, Dr. Richard A., 111
Patterson's Curse, 57, 58, 59, 96, 99, 186
Paulars, 9
peach leaves, 58

Peak Hill (Graham's Station), 25
pears, 61
peas, 52, 103
Perrindales, 20
pessary, 166
pH, 5, 24, 29, 34, 58, 108, 110, 112
Pharmacological Basis of Therapeutics, 122
Phosmet, 150
phosphate, 92, 113
phosphatic fertilizers, 28, 31, 48
phosphorous, 64, 69, 70, 74, 92, 173-74
photosensitization, 119
pig industry, 43
pigs, 33, 113, 121, 125
pin worms (nematodes), 190
pine trees, 61
pink eye (conjunctivitis, ophthalmia, sandy blight), 117, 171
Piperizane, 190
Plaster of Paris, 160
pneumonia, 125, 168
Poisonous Plants in Australia, 173
Poll Dorset, 1
Polwarths, 1, 2, 13, 17, 19, 21, 37
polyarthritis (infectious arthritis), 46, 51, 79, 80, 161
poplar trees, 61
Port Jackson, Sydney, 7
potassium, 32, 43, 44, 45, 51, 52, 64, 67, 74, 84, 104, 108, 147, 153
potassium iodide, 102
potato haulm, 58
pregnancy toxemia (twin lamb disease), 44, 170
privet, 58
prolapse, 93, 174
prostate gland, 113
protein, 32, 33
proud flesh, 100
Prusiner, Stanley, 149
Prussic acid, 54, 59, 174
Pseudomonas, 153

Other Books by Pat Coleby . . .

Natural Cattle Care
BY PAT COLEBY

Natural Cattle Care encompasses every facet of farm management, from the mineral components of the soils cattle graze over, to issues of fencing, shelter and feed regimens. *Natural Cattle Care* is a comprehensive analysis of farming techniques that keep the health of the animal in mind. Pat Coleby brings a wealth of animal husbandry experience to bear in this analysis of many serious problems of contemporary farming practices, focusing in particular on how poor soils lead to mineral-deficient plants and ailing farm animals. Coleby provides system-level solutions and specific remedies for optimizing cattle health and productivity. *Softcover, 198 pages. ISBN 0-911311-68-8*

Natural Goat Care
BY PAT COLEBY

Goats thrive on fully organic natural care. As natural browsers, they have higher mineral requirements than other domestic animals, so diet is a critical element to maintaining optimal livestock health. In *Natural Goat Care*, consultant Pat Coleby shows how to solve health problems both with natural herbs and medicines and the ultimate cure, bringing the soil into healthy balance. Topics include: correct housing and farming methods; choosing the right livestock; diagnosing health problems; nutritional requirements and feeding practices; vitamins and herbal, homeopathic and natural remedies; psychological needs of goats; breeds and breeding techniques. *Softcover, 374 pages. ISBN 0-911311-66-1*

Natural Horse Care
BY PAT COLEBY

Proper horse care begins with good nutrition practices. Chances are, if a horse needs medical attention, the causes can be traced to poor feeding practices, nutrient-deficient feed, bad farming and, ultimately, imbalanced, demineralized soil. Pat Coleby shares decades of experience working with a variety of horses. She explains how conventional farming and husbandry practices compromise livestock health, resulting in problems that standard veterinary techniques can't properly address. *Natural Horse Care* addresses a broad spectrum of comprehensive health care, detailing dozens of horse ailments, discussing their origins, and offering proven, natural treatments. *Softcover, 164 pages. ISBN 0-911311-65-3*

To order call 1-800-355-5313
or order online at www.acresusa.com

Also from Acres U.S.A.

Reproduction & Animal Health

BY CHARLES WALTERS & GEARLD FRY

This book represents the combined experience and wisdom of two leaders in sustainable cattle production. Gearld Fry offers a lifetime of practical experience seasoned by study and observation. Charles Walters draws on his own observations as well as interviews with thousands of eco-farmers and consultants over the past four decades. The result is an insightful book that is practical in the extreme, yet eminently readable. In this book you will learn: how to "read" an animal, what linear measurement is, why linear measurement selects ideal breeding stock, the nuances of bull fertility, the strengths of classic cattle breeds, the role of pastures, the mineral diet's role in health. *Softcover, 222 pages. ISBN 0-911311-76-9*

Homeopathy for the Herd

BY C. EDGAR SHAEFFER, V.M.D.

Subtitled *A Farmer's Guide to Low-Cost, Non-Toxic Veterinary Cattle Care,* this new information-packed book by *Acres U.S.A.'s* Natural Vet will tell you what you need to know to get started in the use of homeopathic medicines with cows. Using case studies and practical examples from both dairy and beef operations, Dr. Shaeffer covers such topics as: creating a holistic operation; organics and homeopathy; prescribing; mastitis and fertility-related problems; and the *Materia Medica,* keynotes and nosodes. Also includes a convenient section that lists specific conditions and remedies. *Softcover, 222 pages. ISBN 0-911311-72-6*

Herd Bull Fertility

BY JAMES E. DRAYSON

James Drayson spent a lifetime researching and teaching about cattle breeding and fertility, with 35 years of experience in measuring bulls from a fertility standpoint. He followed 1,500 bulls from birth to death and recorded findings that are unequaled by any other researcher. *Herd Bull Fertility* will teach you how to recognize whether a bull is fertile even before the semen test. This manual, generously illustrated with photographs and diagrams, is a must for the cattle grower choosing a bull for his breeding program. *Softcover, 135 pages. ISBN 0-911311-73-4*

To order call 1-800-355-5313
or order online at www.acresusa.com

Alternative Treatments for Ruminant Animals

BY PAUL DETTLOFF, D.V.M.

Drawing on 36 years of veterinary practice, Dr. Paul Dettloff presents an natural, sustainable approach to ruminant health. Copiously illustrated chapters "break down" the animal into its interrelated biological systems: digestive, reproductive, respiratory, circulatory, musculoskeletal and more. Also includes a chapter on nosodes, with vaccination programs for dairy cattle, sheep and goats. An information-packed manual from a renowned vet and educator. *Softcover, 260 pages. ISBN 0-911311-77-7*

Grass, the Forgiveness of Nature

Exploring the miracle of grass, pastures & grassland farming

BY CHARLES WALTERS

What is the most important plant in the world? In terms of nutritive content, function within the ecosystem, and even medicinal properties, the answer to this question may very well be *grass*. In this wide-ranging survey of grass forages and pastureland, Charles Walters makes the case that grass is not just for cows and horses — that in fact it is the most nutritious food produced by nature, as well as the ultimate soil conditioner. You will learn from traditional graziers who draw on centuries of wisdom to create beautiful, lush, sustainable pastures, as well as cutting-edge innovators who are using such methods as biodynamics and sea-solids fertilization to create some of the healthiest grasslands in the world. Leading agronomists not only explain the importance of grasses in our environment, they also share practical knowledge such as when to look for peak levels of nutrition within the growing cycle and how to use grass to restore soil to optimum health. A must-read for anyone interested in sustainable, bio-correct agriculture, this information-packed volume is a comprehensive look at an essential family of plants. *Softcover, 320 pages. ISBN 0-911311-89-0*

Soil, Grass & Cancer

BY ANDRÉ VOISIN

Almost a half-century ago, André Voisin had already grasped the importance of the subterranean world. He mapped the elements of the soil and their effects on plants, and ultimately, animal and human life as well. He saw the hidden danger in the gross oversimplification of fertilization practices that use harsh chemicals and ignore the delicate balance of trace minerals and nutrients in the soil. With a volume of meticulously researched information, Voisin issues a call to agricultural scientists, veterinarians, dietitians and intelligent farmers to stand up and acknowledge the responsibilities they bear in the matter of public health. He writes as well to the alarmed consumer of agricultural products, hoping to spread the knowledge of the possibilities of protective medicine — part of a concerted attempt to remove the causes of ill health, disease and, in particular, cancer. *Softcover, 368 pages. ISBN 0-911311-64-5*

The Keys to Herd Health

BY JERRY BRUNETTI

Whether dairy or beef, a healthy herd begins in such keystone concepts as biodiversity on the farm, acid/alkali balance in feedstuffs, forage quality, and more. In this accessible video, eco-consultant and livestock feed specialist Jerry Brunetti details the keynote essential for successful livestock operation. A popular speaker at eco-farming events across North America, Brunetti explains the laws of nature in terms farmers can embrace, and doles out specific steps you can utilize on your farm right away — all in a convenient video format that you can watch and review whenever you like. *VHS & DVD format.*

Holistic Veterinary Care

BY JERRY BRUNETTI & HUBERT J. KARREMAN, V.M.D.

Dr. Hubert J. Karreman, author of the compendium *Treating Dairy Cows Naturally,* is joined by renowned animal nutrition expert Jerry Brunetti to present an overview of the strategies and tools available for successful holistic herd health management. The emphasis is on natural alternatives for the treatment of common dairy cow problems, including complications in reproduction, birth and lactation. This video will provide you with a basic understanding of the power and the limitations of herbs, how to treat the whole cow, and how to build a herbal medicine kit for your farm. Drawing on actual case studies, which are examined, diagnosed, and treated using holistic protocols, this video serves as a virtual hands-on course in holistic herd health that will prove invaluable to every dairy producer, from the micro-scale family farmer to commercial-scale operations. *VHS & DVD format.*

The Other Side of the Fence — Historic Video

WITH WILLIAM A. ALBRECHT, PH.D.

Professor William A. Albrecht's enduring message preserved and presented for future generations. In this 1950s-era film, with introductory and closing remarks by Acres U.S.A. founder Charles Walters, Prof. Albrecht explains the high cost of inadequate and imbalanced soil fertility and how that "dumb animal," the cow, always knows which plant is the healthier, even though we humans don't see a difference with our eyes. A period film that is dated in style but timeless in message. Perfect for your group gathering. *VHS & DVD format, 26 minutes.*

Soil Fertility & Animal Health — The Albrecht Papers, Vol. II

BY WILLIAM A. ALBRECHT, PH.D.

William A. Albrecht, Ph.D. Albrecht was the premier soil scientist and was dismayed by the rapid chemicalization of farming that followed WWII. This book is a well-organized explanation of the relationship between soil fertility and animal and human health. This a great book for those just familiarizing themselves with these concepts and the perfect companion to *Eco-Farm. Softcover, 192 pages. ISBN 0-911311-07-6*

Eco-Farm: An Acres U.S.A. Primer

BY CHARLES WALTERS

In this book, eco-agriculture is explained — from the tiniest molecular building blocks to managing the soil — in terminology that not only makes the subject easy to learn, but vibrantly alive. Sections on NP&K, cation exchange capacity, composting, Brix, soil life, and more! *Eco-Farm* truly delivers a complete education in soils, crops, and weed and insect control. This should be the first book read by everyone beginning in eco-agriculture . . . and the most shop-worn book on the shelf of the most experienced. *Softcover, 476 pages. ISBN 0-911311-74-2*

Weeds: Control Without Poisons

BY CHARLES WALTERS

For a thorough understanding of the conditions that produce certain weeds, you simply can't find a better source than this one — certainly not one as entertaining, as full of anecdotes and homespun common sense. It contains a lifetime of collected wisdom that teaches us how to understand and thereby control the growth of countless weed species, as well as why there is an absolute necessity for a more holistic, eco-centered perspective in agriculture today. Contains specifics on a hundred weeds, why they grow, what soil conditions spur them on or stop them, what they say about your soil, and how to control them without the obscene presence of poisons, all cross-referenced by scientific and various common names, and a new pictorial glossary. *Softcover, 352 pages. ISBN 0-911311-58-0*

To order call 1-800-355-5313
or order online at www.acresusa.com

Mainline Farming for Century 21

BY DAN SKOW, D.V.M. & CHARLES WALTERS

This book demolishes the mythology on which toxic chemical agriculture has been built. Dr. Dan Skow's teacher was the late Dr. Carey Reams, and the lessons he learned — and improved upon — are important ones. This book teaches how to measure fertility down to the atomic level and project forward bins and bushels with brix high enough to confer immunity to fungal, bacterial and insect attack — and to ward off weeds. The biological theory of ionization as applied to agriculture for all to understand. Practical, hands-on advice that is hard to come by. *Softcover, 206 pages. ISBN 0-911311-27-0*

The Non-Toxic Farming Handbook

BY PHILIP A. WHEELER, PH.D. & RONALD B. WARD

In this readable, easy-to-understand handbook the authors successfully integrate the diverse techniques and technologies of classical organic farming, Albrecht-style soil fertility balancing, Reams-method soil and plant testing and analysis, and other alternative technologies applicable to commercial-scale agriculture. By understanding all of the available non-toxic tools and when they are effective, you will be able to react to your specific situation and growing conditions. Covers fertility inputs, in-the-field testing, foliar feeding, and more. The result of a lifetime of eco-consulting. *Softcover, 236 pages. ISBN 0-911311-56-4*

How to Grow World Record Tomatoes

BY CHARLES H. WILBER

For most of his 80+ years, Charles Wilber has been learning how to work with nature. In this almost unbelievable book he tells his personal story and his philosophy and approach to gardening. Finally, this Guinness world record holder reveals for the first time how he grows record-breaking tomatoes and produce of every variety. Detailed step-by-step instructions teach you how to grow incredible tomatoes — and get award-winning results with all your garden, orchard, and field crops! Low-labor, organic, bio-intensive gardening at its best. *Softcover, 132 pages. ISBN 0-911311-57-2*

Bread from Stones

BY JULIUS HENSEL

This book was the first work to attack Von Liebig's salt fertilizer thesis, and it stands as valid today as when first written over 100 years ago. Conventional agriculture is still operating under misconceptions disproved so eloquently by Hensel so long ago. In addition to the classic text, comments by John Hamaker and Phil Callahan add meaning to the body of the book. Many who stand on the shoulders of this giant have yet to acknowledge Hensel. A true classic of agriculture. *Softcover, 102 pages. ISBN 0-911311-30-0*

The Biological Farmer

BY GARY F. ZIMMER

Biological farmers work with nature, feeding soil life, balancing soil minerals, and tilling soils with a purpose. The methods they apply involve a unique system of beliefs, observations and guidelines that result in increased production and profit. This practical how-to guide elucidates their methods and will help you make farming fun and profitable. *The Biological Farmer* is the farming consultant's bible. It schools the interested grower in methods of maintaining a balanced, healthy soil that promises greater productivity at lower costs, and it covers some of the pitfalls of conventional farming practices. Zimmer knows how to make responsible farming work. His extensive knowledge of biological farming and consulting experience come through in this complete, practical guide to making farming fun and profitable. *Softcover, 352 pages. ISBN 0-911311-62-9*

Fertility from the Ocean Deep

BY CHARLES WALTERS

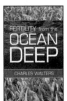
With the recent republication of Dr. Maynard Murray's *Sea Energy Agriculture,* readers discovered the forgotten legacy of an eco-ag pioneer. Murray's idea — that ocean water contains a concentrated, perfect balance of trace minerals in bioavailable form — seems almost as revolutionary today as when he introduced it 30 years ago. In this fascinating book, Charles Walters examines Murray's career and the amazing successes that growers have experienced with his methods, as well as further developments in this technology by creative experimenters. Using hard data obtained in the field, Walters demonstrates that sea-solids fertilizers produce stress-resistant plants and food with naturally extended shelf life and vastly increased nutrient levels. Both an amazing narrative and a practical guide for improving soil and crop health, *Fertility from the Ocean Deep* is a must-read for everyone interested in the cutting edge of agriculture. *Softcover, 175 pages. ISBN 0-911311-79-3*

Sea Energy Agriculture

BY MAYNARD MURRAY, M.D.

Maynard Murray was a medical doctor who researched the crucial importance or minerals — especially trace elements — to plants and animals. Beginning in 1938 and continuing through the 1950s, Dr. Murray used sea solids — mineral salts remaining after water is evaporated from ocean water — as fertilizer on a variety of vegetables, fruits and grains. His extensive experiments demonstrated repeatedly and conclusively that plants fertilized with sea solids and animals fed sea-solid-fertilized feeds grow stronger and more resistant to disease. *Sea Energy Agriculture* recounts Murray's experiments and presents his astounding conclusions. The work of this eco-ag pioneer was largely ignored during his lifetime, and his book became a lost classic — out of print for over 25 years. Now this rare volume is available to a new generation of readers. *Softcover, 109 pages. ISBN 0-911311-70-X*

The Secret Life of Compost

BY MALCOLM BECK, WITH COMMENTARY BY CHARLES WALTERS

We don't need to poison the earth in order to grow better food, and what is harmful to the environment when improperly disposed of often can be turned back to the soil in a beneficial way through composting — if you know how. Here's how. Malcolm Beck's Garden-Ville is one of the largest commercial composting operations in the country. He shares his insight into the processes of decay that can transform everything from lawn trimmings to sewer sludge into life-giving earth. Coupled with Beck's insight into nature and practical advice are remarks from Charles Walters, author and founder of *Acres U.S.A. Softcover, 150 pages. ISBN 0-911311-52-1*

Fletcher Sims' Compost

BY CHARLES WALTERS

Covers the optimal conditions for converting plant and animal wastes into compost by balancing the correct ratio of raw materials, using the correct microorganisms and moisture content, proper pile or windrow construction, and efficient mixing. Fletcher Sims, the Dean of Composters, has elevated the "art" of good composting to a "science." Explains not only the complexities of commercial-scale compost production, but also the benefits of the use of this gentle fertilizer. A book that really draws you in, it is a combination of a biography and technical guide written by the founder of *Acres U.S.A. Softcover, 247 pages. ISBN 0-911311-43-2*

A Farmer's Guide to the Bottom Line

BY CHARLES WALTERS

This book is the culmination of Walters' lifetime of experience, written in his honest, straight-ahead style, outlining how the small farmer-entrepreneur can find his way to a profitable bottom line. The book provides how-to information on each step from planning to implementation of business practices for the eco-friendly farm and includes examples of people who are making a living, and a profit, by demanding a fair price for their labor. Whether you are considering taking up farming as an occupation or just interested in the economics and history of farming, this book is a must-read. *Softcover, 212 pages. ISBN 0-911311-71-8*

To order call 1-800-355-5313
or order online at www.acresusa.com